NELSON Math

GRADE **6**

COPYRIGHT © 2017 by
Nelson Education Ltd.

ISBN-13: 978-0-17-682338-2
ISBN-10: 0-17-682338-7

Printed and bound in Canada
3 4   20   19

Cover Design
Trinh Truong

Cover Image
dcdebs/iStock/Getty Images

Illustrations
Page 51, 61, 112: Coin images
© 2017 Royal Canadian Mint.
All rights reserved.

Contents

REWARD CONTRACT

When you complete a topic in your Nelson Math Workbook, colour in a circle.

My reward will be ...

_____

_____

_____

START

Patterns in Mathematics

Numeration

Data Management

Addition and Subtraction

Measuring Length

Multiplication and Division

Dividing Decimals

Multiplying Decimals

Area

2-D Geometry

3-D Geometry and 3-D Measurement

Fractions, Decimals, Ratios, and Percents

Probability

Patterns and Motion in Geometry

FINISH

Name: _____ Date: _____

Parent/Guardian: _____

Writing Pattern Rules

 Goal Use rules to extend patterns and write pattern rules.

1. Steve learned that a year on Venus is about seven Earth months long.

   a) Complete the table for Venus.

Venus	
Number of years on Venus	Number of months on Earth
1	7
2	
3	
4	

   b) Write a pattern rule to calculate the number of Earth months in any number of years on Venus.

   c) Use your pattern rule to calculate the approximate number of Earth months in 12 years on Venus.

2. Bev saves $12 each month from her paper route.

   a) Write a pattern of numbers that shows the amount Bev saves in 1 to 4 months.

   b) Write a pattern rule to calculate the amount she saves in any number of months.

   c) Use your pattern rule to calculate the amount Bev saves in 10 months.

   d) Bev wants to buy a new hockey jersey for $100. For how many months does she need to save?

At-Home Help

A **pattern** is a group of numbers, shapes, or objects that follow a rule while repeating or changing.

To extend a pattern you can use a table or a pattern rule that relates the term number to the pattern rule.

A **term number** is the number that tells the position of an item in a pattern.

For example, the pattern 2, 4, 6, 8, 10, … can be shown in a table like this:

Term number	Number in pattern
1	2
2	4
3	6
4	8
5	10

A pattern rule to get any number in the pattern is multiply 2 by the term number.

10th term $= 2 \times 10$
$\qquad\quad = 20$

Relationship Rules for Patterns

Goal Write relationship pattern rules based on the term number.

1.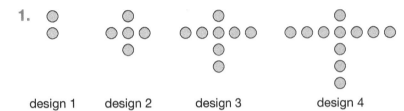

design 1   design 2   design 3   design 4

a) Complete the table to show the number of dots in designs 1 to 4.

Design number	Number of dots
1	2
2	5
3	8
4	11

b) Write the first term and the common difference.

start at 2 and add 3 each Time.

c) How many dots are in design 8?

2,5,8,11,14, 17, 20, 23.
Answer: there are 23 dots in design 8.

2. Determine the 11th term in each pattern. Use a pattern rule. Show your work.

a) 1, 5, 9, 13, ...
17, 21, 25, 29, 33,
47, 42,

c) 2.2, 4.4, 6.6, 8.8, ...
10.10, 12.12, 14.14,
16.16, 18.18, 20.20, 22.22

b) 21, 26, 31, 36, ...
41, 46, 51, 56, 61,
66, 71,

d) $1.25, $1.75, $2.25, $2.75, ...
3.25, 3.75, 4.25,
4.75, 5.25, 5.75,
6.25

Variables in Expressions

 Goal Use variables in an expression.

1. Arpita is baking cookies for a school bake sale. One batch of cookies uses 75 g of chocolate chips.

   a) Calculate the number of grams of chocolate chips in the first four batches of cookies.

   b) Write an explicit pattern rule for the number of grams of chocolate chips in the 10th batch.

   c) Write your pattern rule using a variable for the batch number. Use the variable *b*.

   d) Calculate the number of grams of chocolate chips in the first four batches using your answer in part **c)**. Show your work.

   e) How many grams of chocolate chips does Arpita need to make 11 batches of cookies?

At-Home Help

A **variable** is a letter or symbol that is used to show a quantity. This quantity can have different values.

For example, *t* is a variable that could be used to represent the amount of time you surf the Internet each day.

Variables are usually used when writing explicit pattern rules to make the rules easier to write.

For example, an explicit pattern rule for the pattern 50, 100, 150, 200, … is $50 \times n$. The variable *n* is the term number.

Term (*n*)	Value ($50 \times n$)
1	$50 \times 1 = 50$
2	$50 \times 2 = 100$
3	$50 \times 3 = 150$

Representing Patterns on a Graph

 Goal **Represent patterns in tables and on graphs.**

1. George buys baseballs in packages of 6.

   a) Complete the table to show the total number of baseballs in 0 to 6 packages.

Number of packages	Number of baseballs

   b) Graph the number of baseballs compared to the number of packages.

   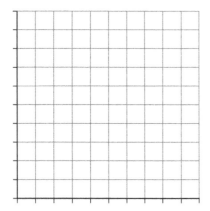

   c) Write a pattern rule to calculate the number of baseballs in any number of packages. Use the variable *n* in your rule.

   d) Determine the number of baseballs in 15 packages.

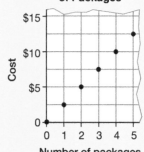

Patterns and Spreadsheets

 Goal Create patterns using spreadsheets and compare the growth.

Pamela wants to know how much money she would have if her bank tripled her money every day for 30 days. She starts with $2.

1. Complete the table or spreadsheet to show a pattern for Pamela's money.

	A	B
1	Day number	Amount
2		
3		
4		
5		

2. What is the formula for calculating the amount on day 4?

3. **a)** Predict the amount Pamela would have on day 14.

   b) Calculate the amount on day 14.

   c) How close was your prediction?

4. Describe the pattern in the amounts Pamela would have.

Solve a Simpler Problem

 Goal   Solve problems by using a simpler problem.

1. Use this pattern.

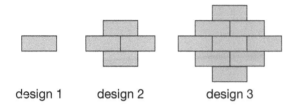

design 1   design 2   design 3

a) How many boxes are in design 8? Make a plan to solve the problem.

At-Home Help

To solve some problems, it is easier to solve a simpler problem.

Make a Plan
Organize data using the simpler problem. If possible, use a table to arrange numbers and drawings.

Carry Out the Plan
Look for a pattern to relate the columns in your table.

Try to find an operation that works for all the rows in your table.

Write a pattern rule.

Check that your pattern rule works for the next simple problem. Draw a picture, if necessary, to check.

Use the pattern rule to solve the original problem.

Carry out your plan.

b) How many boxes are in design 10?

Equal Expressions

 Goal Write equal expressions and determine the value of a missing term in an equation.

1. Which expressions are equal? Use an equals sign. If they are not equal, change one expression to make them equal.

   a) $2 + 3$ ☐ $5 + 0$

   b) $1 + 7$ ☐ $2 + 5$

   c) $8 + 6$ ☐ $2 + 9$

   d) $3 + 8$ ☐ $6 + 5$

2. Replace each ☐ so the expressions are equal.

   a) $5 +$ ☐ $= 7 + 6$

   ☐ $=$ ___

   b) $9 - 4 =$ ☐ $+ 3$

   ☐ $=$ ___

   c) ☐ $\times 3 = 2 + 7$

   ☐ $=$ ___

   d) $12 \div$ ☐ $= 4 \times 3$

   ☐ $=$ ___

3. Isabelle has five swim practices and three soccer practices this month. Judy has the same number of practices this month. Judy has two swim practices.

   a) Write an expression for the number of practices Isabelle has.

   b) Write an expression for the number of practices Judy has.

   c) Write an equation with your expressions.

   d) How many soccer practices does Judy have? Explain what you did.

Variables in Equations

 Goal Solve equations including symbols representing variables.

1. A gym has twice as many soccer balls as basketballs. Altogether there are 36 balls.

   a) Explain what is represented by the equation $S + B = 36$.

   b) Explain what is represented by the equation $S = B + B$.

   c) How many basketballs are there? How many soccer balls are there?

2. In a granola recipe, there is three times as much oats as coconut. The total mass of oats and coconut is 600 g.

   a) Explain what is represented by the equation $O + C = 600$.

   b) Explain what is represented by the equation $O = C + C + C$.

   c) How many grams of each ingredient are there?

Test Yourself   Page 1

Circle the correct answer.

1. One movie ticket costs $5.50. Which table shows the correct pattern?

A.

Number of tickets	Cost
1	$5.50
2	$10.00
3	$15.50
4	$20.00

C.

Number of tickets	Cost
1	$5.50
2	$6.50
3	$7.50
4	$8.50

B.

Number of tickets	Cost
1	$5.50
2	$11.00
3	$16.50
4	$22.00

D.

Number of tickets	Cost
1	$0
2	$5.50
3	$11.50
4	$16.50

2. Which pattern rule best represents the pattern in Question 1?

   A. Add $5.50 to the term number.   **C.** Multiply $5.50 by the term number.

   B. Multiply $5.50 by 2.   **D.** Add 1 to $5.50.

3. What is the cost of six movie tickets in Question 1?

   A. $27.50   **C.** $33.00

   B. $30.00   **D.** $33.50

4. Which pattern rule shows the total number of candies in any number of packages?

Number of packages	Total number of candies
1	3
2	6
3	9
4	12
5	15

   A. $2 \times n$

   B. $3 \times n$

   C. $2 + n$

   D. $3 + n$

5. What is the common difference in the pattern 18, 21, 24, 27, …?

   A. 2   **C.** 4

   B. 3   **D.** 5

6. What is the first term and the common difference in the pattern $1.50, $3.00, $4.50, $6.00, ...?

   A. $1.50, $1.50

   B. $1.50, $3.00

   C. $3.00, $1.50

   D. $1.50, $2.00

7. What is the 10th term in the pattern in Question 6?

   A. $12.00

   B. $13.00

   C. $14.00

   D. $15.00

8. Which expressions are *not* equal?

   A. 2 + 8 and 6 + 4

   B. 9 − 5 and 2 × 2

   C. 3 × 4 and 8 + 2

   D. 7 + 1 and 10 − 2

9. Tilo has two red baseball caps and five green baseball caps. Michael has the same total number of baseball caps as Tilo. Michael has three green baseball caps. Which equation would you use to solve this problem?

   A. 3 + 5 = 2 + c

   B. 2 + 3 = 5 + c

   C. 2 + c = 5 + 3

   D. 2 + 5 = c + 3

10. How many red baseball caps does Michael have in Question 9?

    A. 2

    B. 3

    C. 4

    D. 5

11. A closet has three times as many hats as sweaters. The total number of hats and sweaters is 12. How many of each item is there?

    A. 8 hats, 4 sweaters

    B. 9 hats, 3 sweaters

    C. 7 hats, 5 sweaters

    D. 6 hats, 6 sweaters

Exploring Greater Numbers

 Goal   Compare numbers to one million.

A bumblebee can flap its wings about 200 times per second.

A dragonfly can flap its wings about 38 times per second.

1. Predict how many times a dragonfly flaps its wings in 1000 s.

At-Home Help

A **million** is a number that is 1000 thousands.
1 000 000

To estimate an answer to a problem, use numbers that are close to the values in the problem that are easier to work with.

For example, if a problem involves comparing times in weeks to years, use about 50 weeks in a year.

2. About how many hours would it take for a dragonfly to flap its wings 1 000 000 times? Show your work.

3. **a)** About how many times can a bumblebee flap its wings in 1000 min?

   b) How many 1000 thousands is your answer in part **a)**?

Reading and Writing Numbers

 Goal **Read, write, and describe numbers greater than 100 000.**

1. Write each number in standard and expanded form.

   a)

Millions			Thousands			Ones		
Hundreds	Tens	Ones	Hundreds	Tens	Ones	Hundreds	Tens	Ones
			●●		●●●●		●	

   b)

Millions			Thousands			Ones		
Hundreds	Tens	Ones	Hundreds	Tens	Ones	Hundreds	Tens	Ones
		●	●●●●●	●●	●●●●●●●●●		●●	●●●●●●●●

2. Write each number as a numeral in standard form.

   a) four hundred forty thousand twenty-six

   b) twenty-two thousand eight

   c) seven hundred thirty-one thousand three hundred five

3. Write the words for each number.

   a) 304 000 _____

   b) 21 000 _____

   c) 12 600 _____

4. The sun in our solar system takes about 240 million years to orbit once around the centre of the Milky Way galaxy. Write that number of years in standard form.

Comparing and Ordering Numbers

 Goal Compare and order numbers to 1 000 000.

1. Compare each pair of numbers.
   Use an inequality sign.

   a) 602 589 ☐ 640 077

   b) 314 806 ☐ 409 116

   c) 584 192 ☐ 521 009

2. Order the numbers in Question 1 from least
   to greatest.

3. List three numbers between 216 534 and 242 189.

4. a) The number 5☐8 206 is between ☐96 872 and 512 093. The two missing digits
   are different. What might they be?

   b) Order the numbers from part **a)** from least to greatest.

Renaming Numbers

 Goal **Rename numbers using place value concepts.**

1. Complete each statement.

   a) 4 625 239 is about _____ millions.

   b) 276 081 is about _____ millions.

   c) 3 910 245 is about _____ thousands.

2. Irene takes pictures with her digital camera.
   The file sizes of four of her pictures are:
   3.2 MB 720 kB 21 500 bytes 408 350 bytes

   a) Write the first two file sizes as a number of bytes.

   b) Estimate each file size, except for the first one,
   as millions of bytes or megabytes.

   c) Which photo uses the most bytes?

3. Write each number in another form.

   a) 1.9 million = _____ ones

   b) 4.6 million = _____ thousands

   c) 0.28 million = _____ hundreds

Communicate About Solving Problems

 Goal **Explain your thinking when solving a problem.**

A city produced 183 million kilograms of landfill waste in 2016. In 2017, a composting program reduced the landfill waste to 45 million kilograms. About how much less waste was taken to the landfill each day in 2017? Explain how you solved the problem.

Reading and Writing Decimal Thousandths

 Goal Read, write, and model decimals.

1. Write each fraction as a decimal.

   a) $\dfrac{29}{1000}$ **b)** $\dfrac{503}{1000}$ **c)** $\dfrac{790}{1000}$

2. Colour a 1000ths grid to represent each fraction.

   a) $\dfrac{29}{1000}$ **b)** $\dfrac{503}{1000}$

   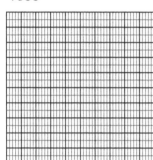   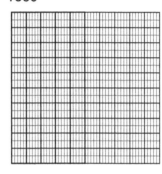

3. Write a decimal for each number.

   a) fifty-two hundreths _____

   b) fifty-two thousandths _____

4. Write a decimal to fit each description.

   a) one-tenth less than 6.302

   b) one-thousandth greater than 6.302

   c) one-hundredth greater than 6.302

5. Write each answer in Question 3 in expanded form.

   a)   **c)**

   b)

6. List two fractions that are equivalent to 0.400.

At-Home Help

Decimal numbers can be modelled using a grid.

For example, 203 thousandths can be represented as

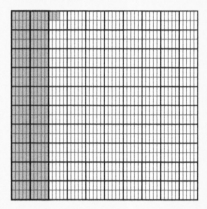

203 thousandths is written as 0.203 in standard form.

In expanded form, the decimal number is 2 tenths + 3 thousandths.

0.203 can also be written as a fraction.

$0.203 = \dfrac{203}{1000}$

Rounding Decimals

 Goal Interpret rounded decimals and round decimals to the nearest tenth or hundredth.

1. Round each decimal to the nearest hundredth.

    a) 0.526

    c) 0.078

    b) 0.896

    d) 3.006

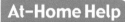

At-Home Help

Decimal numbers can be rounded to the nearest tenth or hundredth.

For example, 0.286 rounds up to 0.29 (decimal hundredth) and 0.3 (decimal tenth).

A number line helps with rounding.

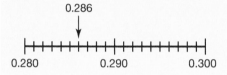

2. Round each decimal to the nearest tenth.

    a) 0.72

    c) 2.462

    b) 1.073

    d) 0.98

3. Which numbers below round to the same hundredth?
   2.417   2.423   2.024   2.400

4. Name a decimal thousandth that could be rounded as described below.

    a) up to 0.35 or down to 0.3

    b) down to 2.12 or down to 2.1

5. Maya cut strips of fabric to make a quilted design. Each piece measured 0.365 m. If she had measured to the nearest centimetre instead, what might the length of fabric be?

Comparing and Ordering Decimals

 Goal **Compare and order decimals to thousandths.**

1. Which decimal is greater?

   a) 2.03 or 2.4

   c) 0.526 or 1.004

   b) 5.7 or 3.99

   d) 0.403 or 0.067

2. Order these decimal numbers from least to greatest.

   a) 2.108   0.053   0.872   1.096

   b) 2.085   2.008   3.004   2.805

3. Which measurement is greater?

   a) 0.087 kg or 0.800 kg

   b) 4.312 km or 3567 m

   c) 450 g or 1.088 kg

4. List the numbers of the form ☐.☐☐ between 1.3 and 1.5 that are greater than 140 hundredths.

At-Home Help

To compare and order decimal numbers to thousandths, compare the digits in this order:
- ones
- tenths
- hundredths
- thousandths

You can also compare and order decimals by their positions on a number line.

Circle the correct answer.

1. Which statement is true?

    A. 1 million = 100 thousands

    B. 1 million = 100 000 hundreds

    C. 1 million = 1000 ten thousands

    D. 1 million = 10 hundred thousands

2. Which is the expanded form for 2 506 084?

    A. 2 000 000 + 50 000 + 6000 + 80 + 4

    B. 2 millions + 5 hundred thousands + 6 hundreds + 84 ones

    C. 2 000 000 + 500 000 + 6000 + 80 + 4

    D. 2 millions + 56 hundreds + 84 ones

3. Which inequality is incorrect?

    A. 206 354 < 216 089

    B. 706 821 > 799 035

    C. 907 645 < 980 004

    D. 625 138 < 739 156

4. What is the correct order of the numbers below from least to greatest?
    871 052,   86 304,   280 546,   901 034,   807 621

    A. 86 304, 280 546, 871 052, 807 621, 901 034

    B. 86 304, 280 546, 807 621, 871 052, 901 034

    C. 86 304, 901 034, 871 052, 807 621, 280 546

    D. 280 546, 871 052, 807 621, 901 034, 86 304

5. Which estimate is correct?

    A. 1.7 MB is about 2 million bytes.

    B. 0.4 kB is about 1 thousand bytes.

    C. 3 230 050 bytes is about 300 kB.

    D. 89 400 bytes is about 1 MB.

6. Which description fits for the number 87 640?

    A. eighty-seven thousand sixty-four

    B. eight hundred seven thousand sixty-four

    C. eight hundred seven thousand six hundred forty

    D. eighty-seven thousand six hundred forty

7. Which math statement is incorrect?

   A. $\frac{52}{1000} = 0.052$

   C. $\frac{79}{1000} = 0.790$

   B. $\frac{206}{1000} = 0.206$

   D. $\frac{358}{1000} = 0.358$

8. Which decimal represents the fraction $\frac{28}{1000}$?

   A. 0.028
   B. 0.280
   C. 0.208
   D. 2.800

9. Which fraction represents the decimal 0.403?

   A. $\frac{43}{100}$
   B. $\frac{43}{1000}$
   C. $\frac{403}{1000}$
   D. $\frac{430}{1000}$

10. Which numbers below round to the same hundredth?
    4.806   3.987   4.813   4.811

    A. 3.987, 4.806, 4.813

    C. 4.806, 4.811, 4.813

    B. 3.987, 4.811, 4.813

    D. 3.987, 4.806, 4.811

11. Which number would be 2.065 rounded to the nearest tenth?

    A. 2.0

    C. 2.5

    B. 2.1

    D. 2.6

12. What is the order of the numbers below from least to greatest?
    1.804,   2.053,   1.692,   0.982,   1.086

    A. 0.982, 1.804, 1.086, 1.692, 2.053

    C. 0.982, 1.086, 1.692, 1.804, 2.053

    B. 0.982, 1.086, 1.804, 1.692, 2.053

    D. 0.982, 1.692, 1.804, 1.086, 2.053

Creating and Analyzing a Survey

 Goal Collect, organize, and display the results of a survey.

Trudy wants to know about TV-watching habits of students in her school. She wrote a question for a survey.

1. How often do you watch TV?
   a) never
   b) once or twice a week
   c) three times a week
   d) more than three times a week
   e) every day

1. What is another survey question Trudy could ask?

2. Trudy asked the students in her school for how long they watch TV at any one time. She recorded the results in a tally chart.

About 1 h	About 2 h	About 3 h	About 4 h	More than 4 h
||||	₶₶ |||	||||	||	||

Sketch a graph to display the results.

3. Explain why you chose the kind of graph you did.

Plotting Coordinate Pairs

 Goal Plot points on a grid and locate them using coordinate pairs.

Yuri is plotting the shape of a stop sign he saw on a street.

1. Plot the points (3, 4), (3, 5), (4, 6), and (5, 6) on the grid. Connect the points in order.

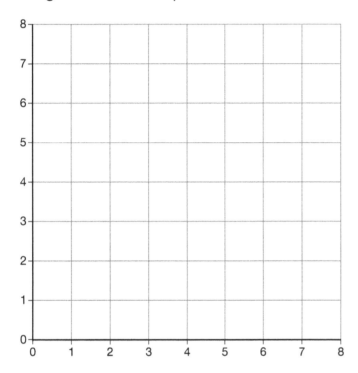

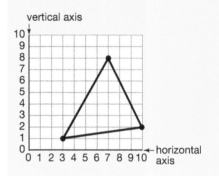
2. Draw the rest of the sign on the grid above.

3. What coordinate pairs did you use to complete the sign?

4. What shape is the sign?

Line Graphs

 Goal **Create and interpret line graphs.**

1. Sui earns money shovelling snow from his neighbour's sidewalk. He wants to know the length of sidewalk he must shovel to earn $5.00. He recorded the distance he shovelled and how much he earned.

Distance (m)	4	8	12	16
Earnings	$1.00	$2.00	$3.00	$4.00

a) Use the data in the table to create a graph.

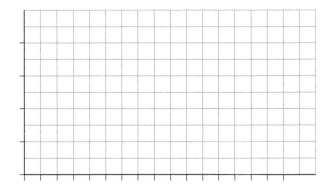

b) Describe how your graph appears.

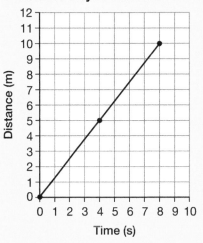
c) Estimate how much Sui earns for a distance of 8.3 m.

d) Predict the distance Sui must shovel to earn $5.00. Explain your reasoning.

Scatter Plots

 Goal **Create and interpret scatter plots.**

The table below shows the low and high daily temperatures in Victoria, British Columbia, for two weeks.

Day	Low temperature (°C)	High temperature (°C)	Day	Low temperature (°C)	High temperature (°C)
Dec. 19	6	12	Dec. 26	5	8
Dec. 20	1	10	Dec. 27	1	8
Dec. 21	1	10	Dec. 28	0	7
Dec. 22	0	8	Dec. 29	1	5
Dec. 23	0	7	Dec. 30	4	8
Dec. 24	4	8	Dec. 31	1	6
Dec. 25	5	8	Jan. 1	0	4

1. Compare the high and low temperatures. Use a scatter plot.

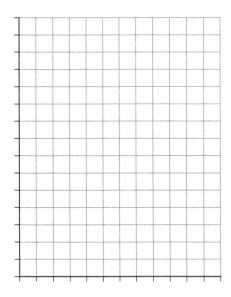

2. Describe how the points appear on the scatter plot. Identify the most common low and high temperatures.

At–Home Help

A **scatter plot** is a graph made by plotting coordinate pairs to show if one set of data can be used to make predictions about another set of data.

For example, the goals and wins of several hockey teams are plotted on the scatter plot below.

Wins Compared to Goals

Each point on this scatter plot is determined using the goals for the first coordinate and the wins for the second coordinate. If a team scored 262 goals and had 43 wins, you would plot the point (262, 43) on the scatter plot.

Mean and Median

 Goal   **Use mean and median to compare sets of data.**

1. Determine the mean and median of each set of numbers.

   a) 8, 0, 2, 7, 1, 7, 3

   b) 2, 3, 6, 0, 0, 1, 1

   c) 7, 0, 9, 0

   d) 18, 11, 22, 9, 5, 0

2. Zoë recorded how long each of her friends walked on two days.

Student	Time on day 1 (min)	Time on day 2 (min)
Clara	20	25
Jose	10	9
Tia	15	18
Nicolas	8	20
Mario	18	19
Tim	5	17
Leah	12	8

   a) Determine the median time for each day.

   b) On which day did the most walking occur?

3. Sara said that the median does not have to be one of the numbers in a set. Is her statement correct? Explain.

At-Home Help

The **median** is the middle number in a set of numbers arranged in order.

For example, the median of 4, 5, 2, 3, 4 is 4.

2   3   **4**   4   5

If the set has an even number of items, the median is halfway between the two middle numbers.

For example, in the set 3, 2, 7, 8, 9, 11, the median is halfway between 7 and 8.

7.5

2   3   7   8   9   11

The **mean** is the sum of a set of numbers divided by the number of numbers in the set. For example, the mean of 3, 4, 5, 2, 2, 3, 2 is $21 \div 7 = 3$.

Changing the Intervals on a Graph

 Goal Describe how changing the number of intervals changes a graph.

Jinji recorded how much his family spent at restaurants during the last year. He sketched a graph of his data.

Month	Amount
Jan.	$40
Feb.	$80
Mar.	$30
Apr.	$64
May	$31
Jun.	$35
Jul.	$45
Aug.	$46
Sept.	$28
Oct.	$48
Nov.	$30
Dec.	$60

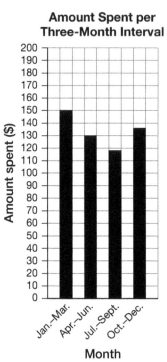

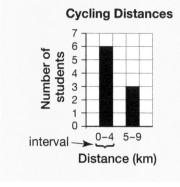
1. Graph Jinji's data.
   Use one-month intervals.

2. Describe the difference between Jinji's graph and your graph.

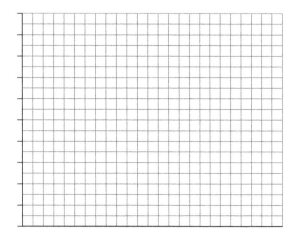

Changing the Scale on a Graph

 Goal Describe how changing the scale changes a line graph.

Charmaine wants to know how fast a bowl of hot soup cools. She measured the temperature of the soup every minute.

Time (min)	0	1	2	3	4	5	6	7	8	9	10
Temperature (°C)	70	68	65	62	58	55	53	51	49	46	45

1. Sketch a line graph of Charmaine's data.

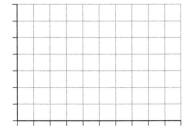

2. What scale did you use for the vertical axis?

   What scale did you use for the horizontal axis?

3. Predict how your graph in Question 1 would change if you doubled the value of each unit on the scale of the vertical axis. Sketch the line graph to check your prediction.

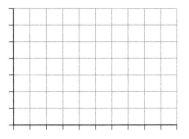

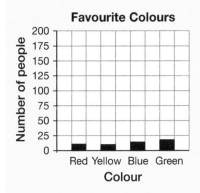
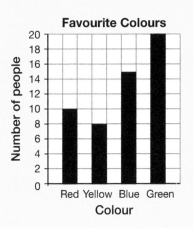

Communicate About Conclusions from Data Displays

 Goal **Use data presented in tables, charts, and graphs to create an argument.**

1. A newspaper printed this scatter plot with the headline "Drinking More Water Means Fewer Colds."

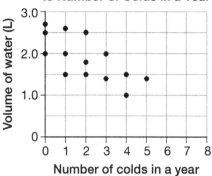

Volume of Water Consumed Compared to Number of Colds in a Year

Write a letter to the editor about the headline and the scatter plot. Use the Communication Checklist.

Constructing Graphic Organizers

 Goal Use Venn diagrams and Carroll diagrams to describe relationships between two sets of data.

Monique wants to know if many countries have both yellow and red on their flags.

Country	Colours on flag
Nigeria	green, white
India	orange, white, red, blue
Philippines	yellow, red, white, blue
Belgium	black, yellow, red
Sweden	blue, yellow
Italy	green, white, red
Canada	red, white
Colombia	yellow, blue, red

1. a) Draw a Venn diagram to sort the countries by flag colour.

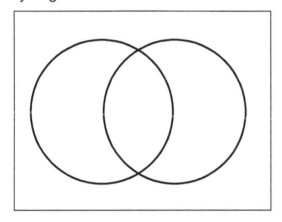

b) Which countries have both yellow and red on their flags?

c) Which country does not have yellow or red?

2. Use the data in the chart above to complete the Carroll diagram.

	1 or 2 colours	More than 2 colours
Red		
Yellow		

At-Home Help

A **Venn diagram** is a drawing with circles inside a rectangle. This type of diagram is helpful when sorting items in a set.

For example, in the Venn diagram below, one circle represents "Dog" and the other circle represents "Cat." Students who have both a dog and a cat are listed where the circles overlap. Since Victor does not have a dog or a cat, his name is listed outside the circles but inside the rectangle.

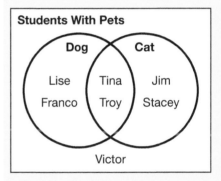

A **Carroll diagram** is a chart that shows relationships using rows and columns.

For example, a Carroll diagram for the data shown in the Venn diagram above would be

	Boy	Girl
Dog	Franco, Troy	Lise, Tina
Cat	Jim, Troy	Stacey, Tina

Test Yourself   Page 1

Circle the correct answer.

1. Mia surveyed 20 students to find out how many hours they surf the Internet each week.

Survey results				
2	5	4	10	5
8	1	3	4	6
7	5	2	3	6
9	3	4	6	7

Which tally chart best represents Mia's data?

A.

Hours	Number of students
0–2 h	IIII
3–4 h	︱︱︱︱
5–6 h	︱︱︱︱
7–8 h	III
9–10 h	III

C.

Hours	Number of students
0–2 h	III
3–4 h	︱︱︱︱ I
5–6 h	︱︱︱︱ I
7–8 h	III
9–10 h	II

B.

Hours	Number of students
0–5 h	︱︱︱︱ ︱︱︱︱ I
6–10 h	︱︱︱︱ IIII

D.

Hours	Number of students
0–5 h	︱︱︱︱ ︱︱︱︱
6–10 h	︱︱︱︱ ︱︱︱︱

2. Which coordinates describe the shape to the right?

   A. (3, 4), (5, 7), (3, 6), (5, 3), (7, 4), and (7, 6)

   B. (4, 3), (7, 5), (6, 3), (3, 5), (4, 7), and (6, 7)

   C. (4, 4), (6, 4), (7, 5), (3, 5), (4, 8), and (6, 8)

   D. (4, 4), (4, 6), (5, 7), (5, 3), (8, 4), and (8, 6)

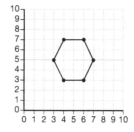

Denise filled a water pitcher with water and then emptied it. Use the line graph to answer Questions 3 and 4.

3. During which time interval is the pitcher being filled?

   A. 0–4 s   **C.** 5–10 s

   B. 0–5 s   **D.** 6–10 s

4. About how long did it take to fill the pitcher with 1 L of water?

   A. about 1 s   **B.** about 2 s

   C. about 3 s   **D.** about 4 s

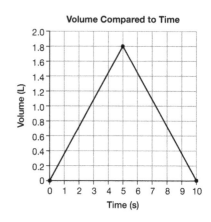

Volume Compared to Time

5. What is the mean and median of this set of numbers?
   5, 13, 9, 15, 8

   A. 10 and 13   **B.** 5 and 9   **C.** 10 and 11   **D.** 10 and 9

6. Katrina timed the distance she cycled each day.

   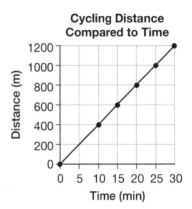

   What would the graph look like if she decreased the value of each unit on the vertical scale?

   A. The graph would look more flat.

   B. The graph would go down more suddenly.

   C. The graph would go up more suddenly.

   D. The graph would look the same.

7. Clive made a Carroll diagram to sort the numbers from 1 to 20. What labels are missing in each column?

	?	?
Less than or equal to 10	4, 8	1, 2, 3, 5, 6, 7, 9, 10
Greater than 10	12, 16, 20	11, 13, 14, 15, 17, 18, 19

   A. Even numbers, Odd numbers

   B. Multiples of 2, Not multiples of 2

   C. Multiples of 3, Not multiples of 3

   D. Multiples of 4, Not multiples of 4

8. Teresa boiled some water for tea, then poured the tea and let it cool down. When did Teresa stop heating the water?

   A. from 0 min to 10 min

   B. at 10 min

   C. from 10 min to 30 min

   D. from 0 min to 30 min

   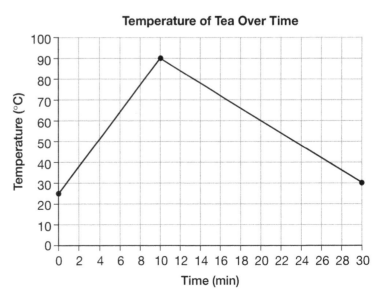

Adding and Subtracting Whole Numbers

 Goal   **Use mental math strategies to calculate sums and differences.**

1. Use mental math to calculate each sum. Describe your strategy.

    a) $680 + 210 =$ _____

    b) $763 + 847 + 289 =$ _____

2. Use mental math to calculate each sum.

    a) $545 + 655 =$ ____   **d)** $715 + 903 + 422 =$ ____

    b) $874 + 926 =$ ____   **e)** $1822 + 428 + 650 =$ ____

    c) $766 + 704 =$ ____   **f)** $2016 + 624 + 910 =$ ____

3. Use mental math to calculate each difference. Describe your strategy.

    a) $680 - 490 =$ ____

    b) $1650 - 95 =$ ____

4. Use mental math to calculate each difference.

    a) $820 - 450 =$ ____   **c)** $903 - 237 =$ ____   **e)** $3005 - 755 =$ ____

    b) $625 - 175 =$ ____   **d)** $1020 - 500 =$ ____   **f)** $2103 - 487 =$ ____

At-Home Help

Rounding is a mental math strategy for adding and subtracting numbers. When you round, you will need to adjust your answer to get the exact answer.

For example:
$23 + 58$ can be rounded to $20 + 60 = 80$. 23 is 3 more than 20 and 58 is 2 less than 60. So adjust your answer by adding 1. The answer is 81.
$76 - 40$ can be rounded to $80 - 40 = 40$. 76 is 4 less than 80. So adjust your answer by subtracting 4. The answer is 36.

Regrouping is another mental math strategy for adding and subtracting numbers. Regroup numbers into 5s or 10s to make calculations easier.

For example:
$43 + 92$ can be regrouped as $(43 + 2) + 90$.
The answer is $45 + 90 = 135$.
$80 - 19$ can be regrouped as $(80 - 10) - 9$.
The answer is $70 - 9 = 61$.

Estimating Sums and Differences

 Goal Estimate sums and differences to solve problems.

1. Which sums are greater than 2200?

   a) 840 + 622 + 713

   b) 372 + 923 + 987

   c) 565 + 834 + 879

   d) 703 + 543 + 824

2. Which differences are less than 540?

   a) 1280 − 640

   b) 6080 − 5590

   c) 4608 − 3024

   d) 8146 − 7870

3. A mountain-climbing contest had teams climb two different mountains. One team climbed Mount Everest. It has a height of 8848 m. Another team climbed Mount Logan in the Yukon Territory. It has a height of 5959 m. About how much higher did the Mount Everest team climb? Describe your strategy.

4. Sam recorded the forms of transportation used by neighbourhood students to get to school. The neighbourhood will win an award if more than 5000 students use a physically active form of transportation to get to school.

Form of transportation	Number of students
walk	3162
bicycle	1072
bus	2154
car	936
other (skateboard, inline skates, etc.)	636

Will Sam's neighbourhood win the award? Describe your strategy.

Adding Whole Numbers

 Goal Solve problems by adding four 3-digit whole numbers.

1. Calculate.

   a)   2 0 6
         3 4 9
         1 2 7
       + 4 6 7

   b)   3 2 9
         4 6 2
         5 0 3
       + 3 6 8

   c)   4 2 1
         2 3 0
         3 2 9
       + 5 4 7

At–Home Help

To add numbers, add digits with the same place value.

Check your answer using estimation.

For example:

```
  1 1
  2 1 3          or    2 1 3
  3 2 7                3 2 7
  1 6 3                1 6 3
+ 2 0 4              + 2 0 4
  9 0 7                8 0 0
                        9 0
                        1 7
                        9 0 7
```

Estimate:
200 + 300 + 200 + 200 = 900

2. During summer camp, Cecilia's group planted trees on five days. The group planted 154 trees on the first day, 183 trees on the second day, 189 trees on the third day, and 196 trees on the fifth day. The group planted a total of 934 trees.

   a) How many trees were planted on the fourth day? Show your work.

   b) Use estimation to check if your answer is reasonable.

3. Balvinder sells chocolate bars to raise money for his school. From Monday to Friday, Balvinder sold $676 worth of chocolate bars. On Monday he sold $117, on Tuesday he sold $130, on Wednesday he sold $143, and on Friday he sold $156. Calculate how much he sold on Thursday. Show your work.

Subtracting Whole Numbers

 Goal **Subtract whole numbers to solve problems.**

1. Estimate and then subtract. Show your work.

   a) 8702 − 6914
   Estimate: more or
   less than 2000?

   _____

   c) 64 902 − 5964
   Estimate: more or
   less than 60 000?

   _____

   b) 10 550 − 9845
   Estimate: more or
   less than 1000?

   _____

   d) 56 003 − 7894
   Estimate: more or
   less than 46 000?

   _____

2. Rico's home town had a population of 75 692 people in 1990. In 2000,
   the population was 83 020 people. By how much did the population increase?
   Determine if your answer is reasonable using estimation. Show your work.

Adding and Subtracting Decimal Numbers

 Goal Use mental math strategies to calculate sums and differences.

Samantha, Matthew, and Akira went to buy some clothes from a charity fundraiser.

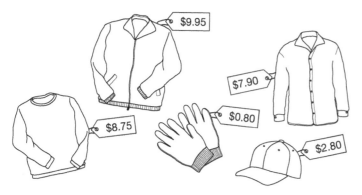

$9.95

$7.90

$0.80

$8.75

$2.80

1. **a)** Samantha has $22.00. Choose three items she can buy.

   b) Use mental math to calculate the total cost. What bills and coins can she use to pay for the items?

   c) Use mental math to calculate Samantha's change.

2. Akira has $18.75 and Matthew has $24.50. How much more money does Matthew have than Akira? Use mental math to calculate your answer.

3. **a)** Choose three items that Akira can buy. Use mental math to calculate the total cost.

   b) Use mental math to calculate Akira's change.

Adding Decimals

 Goal   **Add decimals using base ten blocks and pencil and paper.**

1. Estimate and then add. Show your work.

a) 0.56 + 0.98

d) 3.498 + 2.635 + 0.384

b) 2.804 + 0.426

e) 4.675 + 3.899 + 0.269

c) 0.897 + 5.824

f) 4.8 + 3.152 + 0.59

Subtracting Decimals

 Goal **Subtract decimals using base ten blocks and pencil and paper.**

1. Estimate and then subtract. Show your work.

a) 5.0 − 2.3

d) 6.411 − 2.58

b) 8.21 − 3.63

e) 9.05 − 6.208

c) 4.020 − 1.989

f) 3.8 − 0.058

Communicate About Solving a Multi-Step Problem

 Goal **Explain a solution to a problem.**

Twyla wants to add 1 kg of compost to two vegetable gardens. One garden measures 6.00 m by 3.60 m. The other garden measures 7.60 m by 5.30 m. One kilogram of compost is needed for 43 m^2. Does Twyla have enough compost for both gardens? Write a solution. Determine if your answer is reasonable. Use the Communication Checklist.

Test Yourself Page 1

Circle the correct answer.

1. Using estimation, which question has an answer greater than 1600?

   A. 569 + 872 + 236

   B. 264 + 504 + 429

   C. 379 + 406 + 765

   D. 596 + 604 + 366

Use the survey results to answer Questions 2 and 3.

Favourite food	Number of students
chili	214
pizza	307
curried chicken	234
sushi	209

2. About how many students were surveyed?

   A. about 850   **B.** about 980   **C.** about 800   **D.** about 950

3. How many more students chose pizza than sushi?

   A. 86 students   **B.** 89 students   **C.** 98 students   **D.** 96 students

4. Which calculation is *not* reasonable?

   A. 604 + 392 + 850 + 723 = 2569

   B. 824 − 368 = 456

   C. 356 + 147 + 520 + 801 = 1824

   D. 18 011 − 9234 = 7777

5. What are the missing numbers from top to bottom?

   ```
     6 2 5 2 □
   −   □ 7 □ 3
   □ 3 □ 2 8
   ```

   A. 1, 8, 9, 5, 6   **B.** 1, 8, 9, 5, 7   **C.** 1, 8, 0, 5, 8   **D.** 1, 9, 9, 5, 7

Use the chart to answer Questions 6 and 7.

Juice	Volume (L)
orange	2.615
apple	2.365
cranberry	2.130
mango	3.090

6. What is the total volume of juice?

   A. 10.300 L   **C.** 10.090 L

   B. 10.200 L   **D.** 9.090 L

7. How much more mango juice is there than orange juice?

   A. 1.475 L   **C.** 0.685 L

   B. 1.685 L   **D.** 0.475 L

Use the picture below to answer Questions 8 and 9.

8. What is the total cost of the items shown?

   A. $10.65   **B.** $7.45   **C.** $10.50   **D.** $11.05

9. Kittie bought a can of nuts, a package of dried fruit, and a muffin with a $10 bill. How much change should she receive?

   A. $1.75   **B.** $0.85   **C.** $1.85   **D.** $0.75

10. Jasmine is making a fruit cake. The recipe has a combination of fruits and nuts. What is the total mass of fruit and nuts in the fruit cake?

Ingredient	Mass (kg)
currants	0.450
raisins	0.525
almonds	0.175
candied peel	0.175

    A. 1.200 kg   **B.** 1.325 kg   **C.** 1.550 kg   **D.** 1.860 kg

11. Asgar hiked on two different trails during summer camp. One trail measures 2.863 km. Asgar hiked a total of 5.501 km. How long is the other trail?

    A. 3.738 km   **B.** 3.648 km   **C.** 2.748 km   **D.** 2.638 km

Measuring Length

 Goal **Select an appropriate measuring unit.**

1. State an appropriate unit for each length.

   a) the distance you travel to go to school

   b) the thickness of a coin

   c) the height of a house

   d) the width of a book

2. Explain why you chose the unit you did for one answer in Question 1.

3. Give an example of an item that might be measured in these units.

   a) metres

   b) millimetres

   c) centimetres

   d) kilometres

At-Home Help

The most common units for length used in the metric system are millimetres, centimetres, metres, and kilometres.

When you measure a length, choose a unit that is appropriate for the size of the object.

For example, to measure the height of a tree, use metres or decametres.

To measure the length of a floor tile, use centimetres.

To measure the thickness of a pencil, use millimetres.

To measure the distance between two cities, use kilometres.

1 cm = 10 mm
1 dam = 10 m
1 m = 100 cm
1 km = 1000 m

Metric Relationships

Goal **Interpret and compare measurements with different units.**

1. Rename each measurement using the new unit.

   a) 6.04 cm to millimetres

   b) 7.28 km to metres

   c) 0.591 m to centimetres

   d) 2.006 km to metres

   e) 4.13 m to centimetres

   f) 8.9 cm to millimetres

2. A playground at a community centre is triangular in shape. Calculate the length of the third side.

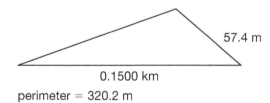

57.4 m

0.1500 km

perimeter = 320.2 m

3. A box of chocolates is in the shape of a regular hexagon. The side length of the hexagon is 6.2 cm. What is the perimeter of the box?

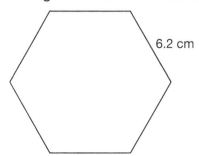

6.2 cm

Perimeters of Polygons

 Goal Measure perimeters of polygons and draw polygons with given perimeters.

You will need a ruler.

1. Measure the perimeter of each polygon.

   a)

   b)

   c)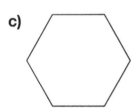

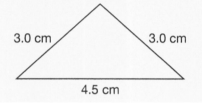
2. Draw two shapes with the same perimeter as the hexagon in Question 1.

Solve Problems Using Logical Reasoning

 Goal Use logical reasoning to solve a problem.

1. **a)** How many numbers between 100 and 600 have a 3 for at least one of the digits?

At-Home Help

Logical reasoning is a process for using information you have to reach a conclusion.

For example, if you know all the students in a class like ice cream and that Jane is in the class, you can logically reason that Jane likes ice cream.

b) How many numbers between 100 and 600 have a 7 for at least one of the digits?

Exploring Perimeter

 Goal **Explore the relationship between perimeter and area measurements.**

1. Vanessa drew a polygon inside a square.

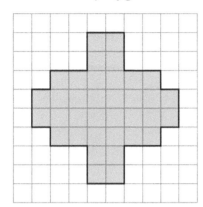

a) Determine the perimeter and the area of the polygon.

b) Draw another polygon with the same area but a different perimeter.

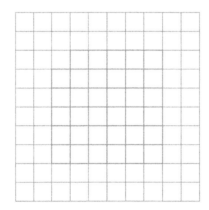

c) Draw another polygon with the same perimeter but a different area.

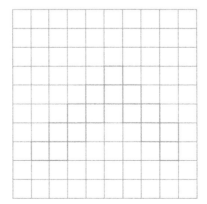

Test Yourself   Page 1

Circle the correct answer.
You will need a ruler.

1. Which unit would be the most appropriate to measure the length of a desk?

   A. millimetres

   B. centimetres

   C. metres

   D. kilometres

2. Which measurement is the same as 0.51 km?

   A. 51 m

   B. 510 m

   C. 5100 cm

   D. 510 000 cm

3. Which measurement is *not* the same as 407 m?

   A. 407 000 mm

   B. 40 700 cm

   C. 4.07 km

   D. 0.407 km

4. What is the length of the fourth side?

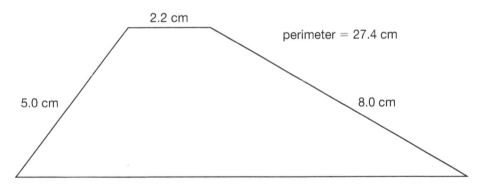

   A. 12.2 cm

   B. 12.3 cm

   C. 12.4 cm

   D. 12.5 cm

5. Patrick drew these polygons actual size. Which polygon has a perimeter of 7.5 cm?

A.

C.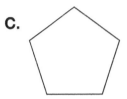

B.

D.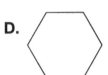

6. What is the perimeter of the polygon shown below?

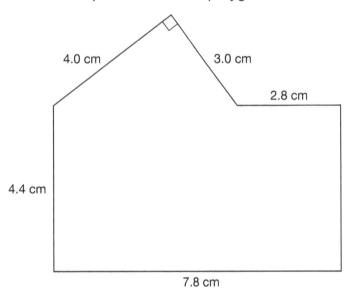

4.0 cm   3.0 cm

2.8 cm

4.4 cm

7.8 cm

A. 25.8 cm   **C.** 26.2 cm

B. 26.0 cm   **D.** 26.4 cm

7. The perimeters of two squares differ by 4.0 cm. The sum of the perimeters for the two squares is 16.0 cm. What is the side length of the larger square?

A. 1.0 cm   **C.** 2.0 cm

B. 1.5 cm   **D.** 2.5 cm

8. When the side length of a regular pentagon is increased, its perimeter increases by 12.5 cm. How much longer is the new side length?

A. 2.0 cm   **B.** 2.5 cm   **C.** 3.0 cm   **D.** 3.5 cm

Identify Factors, Primes, and Composites

 Goal **Identify the factors of prime and composite numbers.**

1. List all the factors of each number.

   a) 16

   b) 45

   c) 31

   d) 22

   e) 18

   f) 60

> **At-Home Help**
>
> A **factor** is a whole number that divides another whole number without a remainder.
>
> For example, 2 is a factor of 8 because 2 divides 8 without a remainder.
>
> $8 \div 2 = 4$
> The factors of 8 are 1, 2, 4, and 8.
>
> A **prime number** is a number that has only two different factors: 1 and itself.
>
> For example, 2 is a prime number because it has only two factors: 1 and 2.
>
> A **composite number** is a number that has more than two different factors.
>
> For example, 4 is a composite number because it has more than two factors: 1, 2, and 4.
>
> The numbers 0 and 1 are neither prime nor composite.

2. Which numbers are prime and which are composite? Show your work.

   a) 41

   b) 15

   c) 21

   d) 12

   e) 19

   f) 25

Identifying Multiples

 Goal Solve problems by identifying multiples of whole numbers.

1. List five multiples of each number.

   a) 4

   b) 10

   c) 22

   d) 9

   e) 11

   f) 40

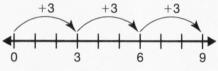

At-Home Help

A **multiple** is a number that is the product of two factors.

For example, 8 is a multiple of 2 because $2 \times 4 = 8$.

To find the multiples of a number, use skip counting or multiplication.

For example:

```
    +3        +3        +3
  ⌒⌒⌒     ⌒⌒⌒     ⌒⌒⌒
◄─┼──┼──┼──┼──┼──┼──┼──┼──┼─►
  0        3        6        9
```

or $3 \times 1 = 3$
$3 \times 2 = 6$
$3 \times 3 = 9$
$3 \times 4 = 12$
and so on.

The multiples of 3 are 3, 6, 9, 12, ….

2. Sergio has 30 gifts numbered from 1 to 30. There is a kite in each gift with a number that is a multiple of 4. There is a baseball cap in each gift with a number that is a multiple of 6.

   a) Which gifts have a kite?

   b) Which gifts have a baseball cap?

   c) Which gifts have both a kite and a baseball cap?

Calculating Coin Values

Goal   Use the relationship between coin values to simplify calculations.

1. Zak has 24 quarters in his coin collection. Sketch an array of these coins to calculate 24 × 25.

2. Calculate the value of each number of coins.

   a) 80 nickels _____

   b) 80 quarters _____

   c) 50 dimes _____

3. **a)** Ramona has 16 nickels, 15 dimes, and 20 quarters. Show one way to arrange each of these coins to calculate the total value of Ramona's coins.

At-Home Help

Multiplication can be used to calculate the value of coins.

For example, to calculate the value of 12 quarters, multiply 12 × 25. Use an array to make the multiplication easier.

For example, two possible arrays for 12 quarters are

In the first array, the value of each row is 50¢, so the multiplication can be done as 6 × 50 = 300.

In the second array, the value of each column is 100¢, so the multiplication can be done as 3 × 100 = 300. Both arrays show that 12 × 25 = 300¢.

   b) Calculate the value for each coin arrangement in part **a)**.

   nickels _____

   dimes _____

   quarters _____

   Total: _____

Multiplying by Hundreds

 Goal Use multiplication facts and regrouping to multiply by hundreds.

1. Calculate.

   a) 100 × 40 = _____

   b) 70 × 200 = _____

   c) 30 × 500 = _____

   d) 800 × 600 = _____

   e) 700 × 900 = _____

   f) 6000 × 60 = _____

2. Jake's class baked 20 batches of cookies. Each batch contained 200 cookies. How many cookies did Jake's class bake? Show your work.

3. Marlie needs to fill 400 cups with juice. Each cup holds 200 mL. How much juice does she need? Show your work.

Estimating Products

 Goal **Estimate to check the reasonableness of a calculation.**

1. Check if each answer is reasonable.
   Use estimation.

   a) 64 × 36 = 3204

   b) 122 × 38 = 4636

   c) 44 × 1045 = 66 980

   d) 78 × 2196 = 171 288

> **At-Home Help**
>
> To check the reasonableness of a calculation, estimate the answer using one or more mental math strategies.
>
> For example: To check if 57 × 52 = 2964 is reasonable, use rounding or a range.
>
> 60 × 50 = 3000
> The product 2964 is reasonable.
>
> or 50 × 50 = 2500
> 60 × 60 = 3600
> The answer should be between 2500 and 3600. The product 2964 is reasonable.

2. **a)** Nirmala rides her bicycle 56 days during the school year. Each of those days, she rides 540 m. Calculate the distance she rides during the school year.

   b) Show that your answer is reasonable. Use estimation.

Multiplying by Two-Digit Numbers

 Goal **Use pencil and paper to multiply a whole number by a two-digit number.**

1. Calculate.

   a) 34 × 123

   c) 81 × 3699

   b) 58 × 256

   d) 77 × 6908

2. Rose delivers newspapers in a seniors' residence. She delivers 23 papers on each floor. There are 12 floors in the building. She makes deliveries 15 times per month.

   a) Do you think Rose delivers more than 3000 newspapers in a month? Explain how you know.

   b) Calculate the number of newspapers Rose delivers in a month. Show your work.

Dividing by 1000 and 10 000

 Goal Use mental math to divide whole numbers by 1000 and 10 000.

1. Calculate. Use mental math.

a) 19 000 ÷ 1000 = _____

b) 36 000 ÷ 1000 = _____

c) 2 080 000 ÷ 10 000 = _____

d) 1 620 000 ÷ 1000 = _____

e) 805 000 ÷ 1000 = _____

f) 40 000 ÷ 1000 = _____

g) 90 000 ÷ 10 000 = _____

h) 6000 ÷ 1000 = _____

At–Home Help

To multiply a whole number by 1000, move all digits to the left three places. You can see the pattern by multiplying by 10, 100, or 1000.

For example,

$3 \times 10 = 30$ $13 \times 1000 = 13\ 000$
$3 \times 100 = 300$ $130 \times 1000 = 130\ 000$
$3 \times 1000 = 3000$ $1300 \times 1000 = 1\ 300\ 000$

To divide a whole number by 1000, move all digits to the right three places.

For example,

$9000 \div 10 = 900$ $98\ 000 \div 1000 = 98$
$9000 \div 100 = 90$ $980\ 000 \div 1000 = 980$
$9000 \div 1000 = 9$ $9\ 800\ 000 \div 1000 = 9800$

2. Leo's binoculars can magnify an object 1000 times.

a) How tall would an object be if the image in the binoculars is 44 000 mm tall?

b) How tall would the image in the binoculars be if the object is 5 mm tall?

Dividing by Tens and Hundreds

 Goal **Use renaming and a division fact to divide by tens and hundreds.**

1. Calculate. Use multiplication to check each answer.

   a) 3000 ÷ 50 = _____

   b) 14 000 ÷ 200 = _____

   c) 45 000 ÷ 300 = _____

   d) 200 000 ÷ 400 = _____

At-Home Help

To divide a whole number by tens or hundreds, you can use renaming.

For example: To divide 60 000 by 200, rename both numbers as hundreds.

60 000 = 6 ten thousands
        = 60 thousands
        = 600 hundreds

   200 = 2 hundreds

60 000 ÷ 200 is the same as 600 hundreds ÷ 2 hundreds.

600 ÷ 2 = 300
So 60 000 ÷ 200 = 300

Check the answer using multiplication.
300 × 200 = 60 000

2. **a)** Kyle and his brother Joe have 24 000 family photos. They saved 600 photos each month. How many months did it take to save the photos?

   b) Use multiplication to check your answer.

Estimating Quotients

 Goal **Use multiplication and rounding to check the reasonableness of a quotient.**

You will need a calculator.

1. Check if each answer is reasonable. Use estimation and multiplication.

   a) 2170 ÷ 31 = 70

   _____

   _____

   b) 6888 ÷ 28 = 194

   _____

   _____

   c) $58\overline{)7656}$ with 132 above

   _____

   _____

   d) $72\overline{)8280}$ with 256 above

   _____

   _____

2. Choose the best estimate for each quotient.

   a) 874 ÷ 26 = _____   10   20   30   40

   b) 657 ÷ 55 = _____   10   20   30   40

   c) 834 ÷ 44 = _____   10   20   30   40

3. The Grade 6 students in Pedro's school are hoping to raise $4000 to buy food for homeless people. There are 84 Grade 6 students in Pedro's school.

   a) Calculate the amount of money each student is hoping to raise. Use a calculator.

   b) Show that your answer is reasonable. Use estimation and multiplication.

Dividing by Two-Digit Numbers

 Goal Divide a four-digit number by a two-digit number.

1. Calculate. Show your work. Check your answers using multiplication.

   a) 1088 ÷ 16

   c) 63)‾4473

   b) 2278 ÷ 34

   d) 81)‾7533

At-Home Help

To divide a four-digit number by a two-digit number, use estimation and multiplication.

For example: To divide 2365 by 43, round 43 to the nearest ten.

43 is close to 40. Use 40 to estimate.

40 × 50 = 2000 is low.

40 × 60 = 2400 is high but very close.

```
        55
  43)2365
      2150     ⟶  43 × 50 = 2150
      ‾‾‾‾
       215
       215     ⟶  43 × 5 = 215
       ‾‾‾
         0
```

To check if a quotient is reasonable, use multiplication or estimation.

For example:
```
      5 5
    × 4 3
    ‾‾‾‾‾
    1 6 5
  2 2 0 0
  ‾‾‾‾‾‾‾
  2 3 6 5
```
Estimate: 60 × 40 = 2400

2. Jamal's class ordered 28 sets of coloured pencils for art projects during the school year. They ordered 1820 pencils altogether.

   a) How many coloured pencils are in a set?

   b) Use estimation to check if your answer is reasonable.

Communicate About Creating and Solving Problems

 Goal Create and explain how to solve multiplication and division problems.

Kiki's family has an energy-efficient washing machine. The machine uses 4620 L of water a year to wash all the laundry. The family washes 7 loads of laundry a month.

1. **a)** Create a multiplication or division problem using the information about Kiki's family.

   b) Explain the solution to your problem in part **a)**. Use the Communication Checklist.

Order of Operations

 Goal **Determine whether the value of an expression changes when the order of calculating changes.**

You will need a calculator.

1. Determine the value of each number statement. Using a calculator, enter each number and operation from left to right.

   a) $16 + 12 - 8 =$ _____

   b) $9 \times 11 \div 3 =$ _____

   c) $16 \div 4 \times 2 + 5 =$ _____

   d) $22 - 9 + 12 - 8 =$ _____

2. **a)** Sonya entered a contest to win a trip to Mexico. She had to answer this skill-testing question:
   $18 \div 2 + 3 \times 7$
   Show how Sonya could get an answer of 30.

   b) Drake had to answer this skill-testing question:
   $3 \times 5 - 21 \div 7$
   Show how Drake could get an answer of 12.

   c) Tilly said the answer to the skill-testing question $45 \div 3 - 7 \times 2$ is 1. Show how she could have got this answer.

Circle the correct answer.

1. What are the factors of 24?

   A. 1, 24

   B. 1, 2, 4, 6, 12, 24

   C. 1, 2, 3, 4, 6, 8, 12, 24

   D. 1, 3, 4, 6, 8, 24

2. Which arrangement best represents 16×25?

   A.

   C.

   B.

   D.

3. During a charity event, 8000 packages of candy were sold.
   Each package had 40 candies. How many candies were sold?

   A. 12 000 candies

   B. 120 000 candies

   C. 32 000 candies

   D. 320 000 candies

4. Using estimation, which answer is *not* reasonable?

   A. $68 \times 68 = 4624$

   B. $82 \times 47 = 3854$

   C. $312 \times 96 = 18\,352$

   D. $23 \times 1867 = 42\,941$

5. Which product is the correct answer to 2481×14?

   A. 21 050

   B. 34 734

   C. 52 901

   D. 68 437

6. Which quotient is incorrect?

   A. $3600 \div 30 = 120$

   B. $81\,000 \div 900 = 90$

   C. $45\,000 \div 50 = 90$

   D. $49\,000 \div 70 = 700$

Multiplication and Division   61

7. Using estimation and multiplication, which answer is reasonable?

   A. 1998 ÷ 37 = 54

   B. 4191 ÷ 33 = 217

   C. $\begin{array}{r} 36 \\ 43\overline{)2408} \end{array}$

   D. $\begin{array}{r} 67 \\ 68\overline{)3196} \end{array}$

8. Which quotient is the correct answer to $54\overline{)4698}$?

   A. 87

   B. 38

   C. 69

   D. 45

9. Which numbers are multiples of 12?

   A. 35, 36, 40, 45

   B. 24, 48, 60, 72

   C. 30, 40, 50, 60

   D. 24, 44, 64, 84

10. What are the answers to 502 000 ÷ 1000 and 14 × 1000?

    A. 5020, 1400

    B. 502, 14

    C. 502, 14 000

    D. 5020, 140

11. Mohammed spends 560 min on the Internet each month. How many hours does he spend on the Internet in a year?

    Which explanation is best to solve the problem?

    A. First I need to multiply 560 by 60 to determine the number of hours Mohammed spends in a month. There are 12 months in a year. So I need to multiply the product by 12.

    B. First I need to multiply 560 by 12 to determine the number of minutes Mohammed spends in a year. There are 60 minutes in each hour. So I need to divide the product by 60.

    C. First I need to divide 560 by 12 to determine the number of minutes Mohammed spends in a year. There are 60 minutes in each hour. So I need to divide the quotient by 60.

    D. First I need to divide 560 by 60 to determine the number of hours Mohammed spends in a month. There are 12 months in a year. So I need to divide the quotient by 12.

Estimating Angle Measures

 Goal **Compare and estimate angle measures.**

You will need a protractor.

1. Estimate the size of each angle.

a)

c)

b)

d)

At–Home Help

You can estimate the size of an angle by comparing it to an angle that you know, such as 45°, 60°, or 90°.

45°

60°

90°

2. Which angles that you know did you use to help you estimate the angles in Question 1? Give reasons for your choices.

a)

c)

b)

d)

3. Measure the angles in Question 1. How close were your estimates?

a)   c)

b)   d)

Investigating Properties of Triangles

 Goal Investigate angle and side relationships of triangles.

You will need a ruler and a protractor.

1. **a)** Without using a protractor, label these angles on the triangles: 60°, 80°, 20°, 80°, 60°, and 60°.

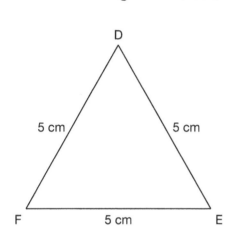

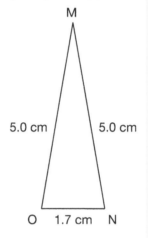

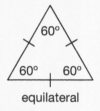

b) Explain how you know the angle sizes for both triangles.

c) Measure the angles with a protractor to check your answer.

2. The angles in triangle PQR are 90°, 35°, and 55°. The side lengths are 5.8 cm, 7.0 cm, and 4.0 cm.

a) Without using a ruler or protractor, label the angle sizes and side lengths.

b) Measure the angles and side lengths to check your answers.

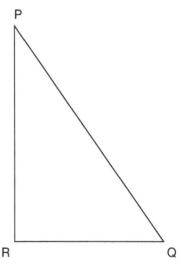

Communicate About Triangles

 Goal **Communicate and explain geometric ideas.**

1.

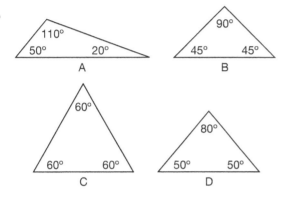

a) Add the angle measures for each triangle.

b) Make a hypothesis about the sum of all the angles in a triangle. Use the Communication Checklist.

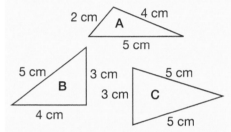
2.

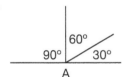 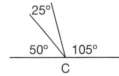

a) Add the angle measures on each line.

b) Make a hypothesis about the sum of the angles on a straight line. Use the Communication Checklist.

Constructing Polygons

 Goal **Construct polygons based on angle measures and side lengths.**

You will need a ruler and a protractor.

1. Draw each polygon. Label all side lengths and angle measures.

   a) equilateral triangle with side lengths of 3 cm and angle measures of 60°

   b) scalene triangle with side lengths of 3 cm, 4 cm, and 5 cm and one angle measure of 90°

   d) parallelogram with angle measures of 120° and 60° and side lengths of 4 cm and 5 cm

   c) rectangle with side lengths of 3 cm and 5 cm

   e) regular hexagon with side lengths of 2 cm and angle measures of 120°

Sorting Polygons

 Goal Sort polygons by line symmetry.

You will need a ruler.

1. **a)** Name each polygon. Draw all the lines of symmetry you can find.

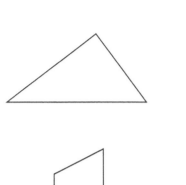 

 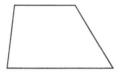 

b) Sort the polygons using a Venn diagram. Choose categories from the property list.

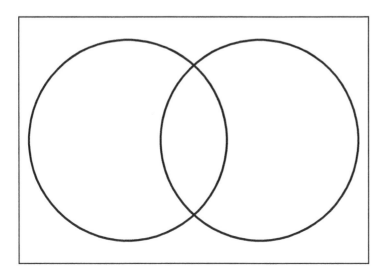

Property list
number of lines of symmetry
number of equal sides
number of equal angles
number of sides
number of angles

Investigating Properties of Quadrilaterals

 Goal Sort and classify quadrilaterals by their properties.

You will need a ruler and a protractor.

1. **a)** Name each quadrilateral.

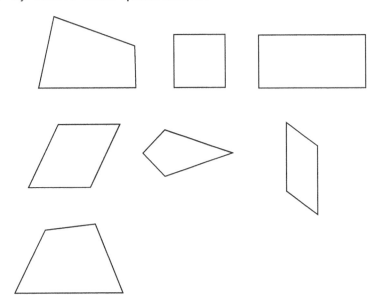

At-Home Help

The diagonals of quadrilaterals have certain properties.

Squares have diagonals that are equal and meet at 90°. Kites and rhombuses have unequal diagonals that meet at 90°.

Rectangles have diagonals that are equal lengths that do not meet at 90°. Parallelograms and some trapezoids have unequal diagonals that do not meet at 90°.

b) Draw all the diagonals in each quadrilateral above. Mark any right angles you find where the diagonals meet.

2. Sort the quadrilaterals using a Venn diagram. Choose categories from the property list.

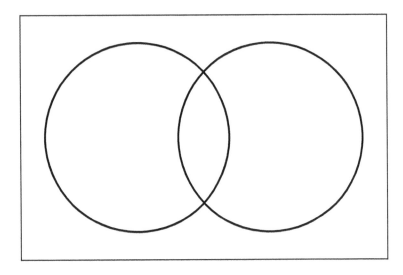

Property list
equal diagonals
unequal diagonals
diagonals that meet at 90°
diagonals that do not meet at 90°

Test Yourself   Page 1

Circle the correct answer.

1. Which angles that you know would you use to estimate these angles?

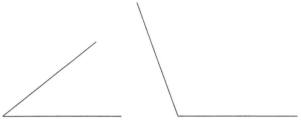 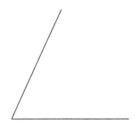

   A. 180°, 90°, 45°   **B.** 45°, 120°, 90°   **C.** 45°, 90°, 60°   **D.** 90°, 60°, 60°

2. The side lengths of the triangle are 10 cm and 14 cm.
   Which side lengths are correct?

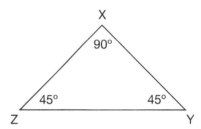

   A. XZ = 14 cm, XY = 10 cm, YZ = 10 cm

   B. XZ = 10 cm, XY = 14 cm, YZ = 10 cm

   C. XZ = 14 cm, XY = 14 cm, YZ = 10 cm

   D. XZ = 10 cm, XY = 10 cm, YZ = 14 cm

3. Which polygons have more than two lines of symmetry?

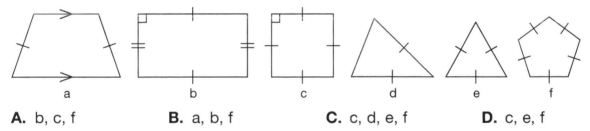

   A. b, c, f   **B.** a, b, f   **C.** c, d, e, f   **D.** c, e, f

4. What information do you need to construct a regular polygon?

   A. all side lengths and all angle measures

   B. one side length and one angle measure

   C. two side lengths and one angle measure

   D. two side lengths and two angle measures

Test Yourself   Page 2

Use the polygons below to answer Questions 5 to 7.

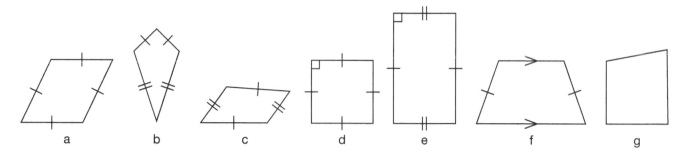

5. Which quadrilaterals have equal diagonals?

   A. d, e, f   **B.** b, c, g   **C.** b, c, f, g   **D.** a, d, e

6. Which quadrilaterals have diagonals that do not meet at 90°?

   A. a, b, d   **B.** a, b, c, d   **C.** c, e, g   **D.** c, e, f, g

7. Which quadrilaterals have diagonals that are unequal but meet at 90°?

   A. b, c, d   **B.** c, e   **C.** a, b   **D.** a, f, g

Unit Relationships

 Goal Identify relationships between and among linear and square metric units.

1. Express each area in square centimetres.

   a) 8 m² = _____   **c)** 3.5 m² = _____

   b) 12 m² = _____   **d)** 0.7 m² = _____

2. Express each area in square metres.

   a) 90 000 cm² = ____   **c)** 43 000 cm² = ____

   b) 660 000 cm² = ____ **d)** 6000 cm² = ____

3. Calculate the area of each shape in square centimetres and square metres. Show your work.

   a)
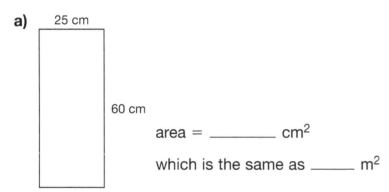

   area = _____ cm²

   which is the same as _____ m²

   b)
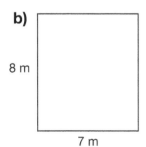

   area = _____ m²

   which is the same as _____ cm²

4. Tina made a paper lantern from a 2 m² sheet of paper. She used a 160 cm by 36 cm piece of the paper. What is the area of paper left over?

Area Rule for Parallelograms

 Goal Develop and use a rule for calculating the area of a parallelogram.

You will need a ruler and a protractor.

1. Calculate the area of each parallelogram.
   Show your work.

a)

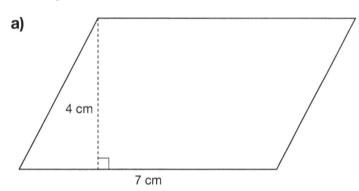

4 cm

7 cm

b)

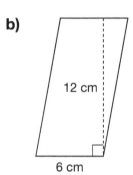

12 cm

6 cm

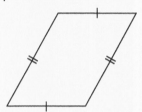
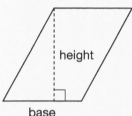
2. Anand drew three parallelograms. Measure the dimensions and calculate the area of each parallelogram. Show your work.

a)

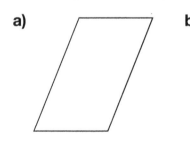

b)

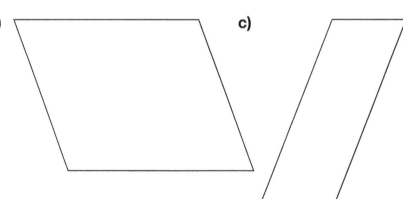

c)

Geometric Relationships

 Goal Identify relationships between triangles and parallelograms.

You will need a ruler.

1. Complete the chart by sketching parallelograms made up of two congruent triangles.

Type of triangle	Sketch of parallelograms
equilateral 4 cm / 4 cm 4 cm	
isosceles 5 cm / 5 cm 3 cm	

2. How is the area of a triangle related to the area of a parallelogram? Explain.

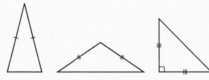

Area Rule for Triangles

 Goal   **Develop and use a rule for calculating the area of a triangle.**

You will need a ruler and a protractor.

1. Calculate the area of each triangle. Show your work.

a)

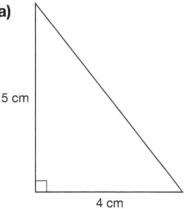

b)

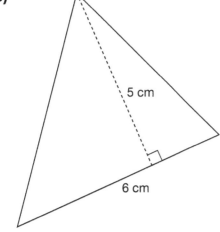

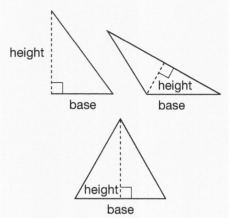
2. Measure each triangle and calculate the area.

a)

b)

Solve Problems Using Open Sentences

 Goal Use open sentences to solve problems.

1. Penelope made a fabric flower using triangles. Each petal has a base of 5 cm and a height of 8 cm.

   She wants to make another flower with twice the area. What base and height could she use for the new petals? Write an open sentence to solve the problem. Show your work.

2. Matt's house has a basement room with an area of 92 m². Matt's parents are planning to build a bathroom in the room. The area of the room will then be 88 m². List two possible sets of whole number dimensions and shapes for the bathroom. Write an open sentence to solve the problem. Show your work.

Areas of Polygons

Goal Calculate the area of polygons by breaking them into simpler shapes.

You will need a ruler.

1. Justin drew a boat using different polygons. Calculate the area of the shape. Show your work.

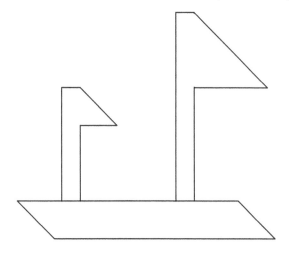

Test Yourself   Page 1

Circle the correct answer.
You will need a ruler.

1. Which measurement is the same as 13 m²?

   A. 1300 cm²   **C.** 130 000 cm²

   B. 13 000 cm²   **D.** 1 300 000 cm²

2. Which measurement is the same as 20 000 cm²?

   A. 0.2 m²   **C.** 20 m²

   B. 2 m²   **D.** 200 m²

3. Which statement is *not* correct?

   A. 80 000 cm² is the same as 8 m².

   B. 0.1 m² is the same as 10 000 cm².

   C. 2500 cm² is the same as 0.25 m².

   D. 31 m² is the same as 310 000 cm².

4. What is the area of the parallelogram in square centimetres?

   A. 12 cm²   **C.** 32 cm²

   B. 16 cm²   **D.** 36 cm²

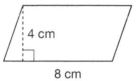

5. How many different parallelograms can you make using these triangles?

   A. 1   **C.** 3

   B. 2   **D.** 4

 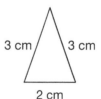

6. Which area relationship is *not* true?

   A. Two congruent triangles can be used to form a parallelogram.
   The area of one triangle is half the area of the parallelogram.

   B. A parallelogram can be used to form a rectangle if it is cut along its height.
   The area of the parallelogram is equal to the area of the rectangle.

   C. The area of a rectangle is equal to the length times the width.

   D. Two congruent triangles can be used to form a parallelogram.
   The area of one triangle is double the area of the parallelogram.

7. What is the area of the triangle?

   A. 10 cm^2 **C.** 20 cm^2

   B. 12 cm^2 **D.** 24 cm^2

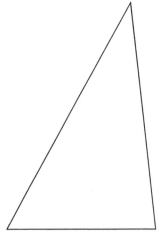

8. Nadia designed a logo using different polygons.
   What is the area of the logo?

   A. 14 cm^2 **C.** 22 cm^2

   B. 15 cm^2 **D.** 36 cm^2

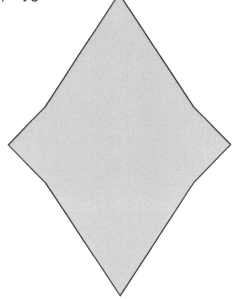

Estimating Products

 Goal **Estimate products of decimal tenths and money amounts using a variety of strategies.**

1. Estimate each product. Show your work.

   a) 3.6 × $29.55

   d) 5.7 × $12.77

   b) 2.4 × $16.59

   e) 6.6 × $24.41

   c) 4.3 × $18.86

   f) 8.4 × $49.48

2. Estimate each cost. Use a method that will give the answer closest to the actual cost.

   a) 1.2 kg at $16.88 per kilogram

   d) 4.3 kg at $29.10 per kilogram

   b) 0.6 kg at $21.77 per kilogram

   e) 5.4 kg at $31.74 per kilogram

   c) 1.8 kg at $18.45 per kilogram

   f) 8.7 kg at $39.25 per kilogram

Multiplying by 1000 and 10 000

 Goal **Multiply decimal tenths, hundredths, and thousandths by 1000 and 10 000.**

1. Calculate.

   a) 1000 × 0.501 = _____

   b) 14.82 × 1000 = _____

   c) 10 000 × 29.086 = _____

   d) 5.8 × 10 000 = _____

   e) 1000 × 67.3 = _____

   f) 4.01 × 1000 = _____

2. Determine the distance in metres.

   a) 51.42 km = _____ m

   b) 0.986 km = _____ m

   c) 8.023 km = _____ m

   d) 18.7 km = _____ m

   e) 30.002 km = _____ m

   f) 84.06 km = _____ m

3. Jamie rides 4.26 km on his bicycle each day.
   About how far does he ride in 3 years?

4. Dana walks about 0.76 m in each step. How far could she travel if she takes
   10 000 steps?

> ### At-Home Help
>
> To multiply a decimal tenth, hundredth, or thousandth by 1000, move all digits to the left three places. To multiply by 10 000, move all digits to the left four places. You can see the pattern by multiplying by 10, 100, 1000, or 10 000.
>
> For example,
> 29.8 × 10 = 298
> 29.8 × 100 = 2980
> 29.8 × 1000 = 29 800
> 29.8 × 10 000 = 298 000

Multiplying Tenths by Whole Numbers

 Goal **Multiply decimal tenths by whole numbers using models, drawings, and symbols.**

1. Multiply. Show your work.

   a) 14.3×5 **c)** 20.7×3

   b) 2.8×6 **d)** 82.4×9

2. A fruit pie uses 1.3 kg of peaches, 50.5 g of ground almonds, and 2 packages of ricotta. Serina needs to make 4 pies for a family gathering.

   a) How much of each ingredient is needed?

   b) One kilogram of peaches costs $6. What is the total cost of the peaches needed?

Multiplying by 0.1, 0.01, or 0.001

 Goal **Multiply by 0.1, 0.01, or 0.001 using mental math.**

1. Multiply.

   a) 245 × 0.01 = _____

   b) 312 × 0.1 = _____

   c) 405 × 0.001 = _____

   d) 67 × 0.01 = _____

   e) 89 × 0.001 = _____

   f) 42 × 0.1 = _____

   g) 540 × 0.01 = _____

   h) 30 × 0.001 = _____

2. Determine the missing measurement.

   a) 45 g = _____ kg

   b) 57 mm = _____ cm

   c) 62 cm = _____ m

   d) 202 m = _____ km

   e) 368 g = _____ kg

   f) 250 mm = _____ cm

3. What is each measurement?

   a) a line of 804 cubes, each 0.01 m long, in metres

   b) a line of 62 boxes, each 0.1 m wide, in metres

   c) a 480 g bag of sunflower seeds, in kilograms

   d) a 22 g candy, in kilograms

Multiplying Multiples of Ten by Tenths

 Goal Multiply to calculate the decimal portion of a multiple of 10.

1. Calculate. Show your work.

    a) 0.3 × 250 = _____

    b) 0.1 × 850 = _____

    c) 0.4 × 530 = _____

    d) 0.6 × 800 = _____

    e) 0.5 × 640 = _____

    f) 0.8 × 2650 = _____

> **At-Home Help**
>
> To multiply a decimal tenth by a whole number, you can write the decimal tenth as a multiple of 10.
>
> For example, 0.4 = 0.1 × 4
> To multiply 0.4 × 320, multiply
> 0.1 × 320 = 32.
> Then multiply 4 × 32 = 128.
> 0.4 × 320 = 128

2. At Neil's family picnic, 10 people ate 0.6 of 6400 g of roast chicken and 0.5 of a 4500 mL container of potato salad.

    a) How much roast chicken did Neil's family eat?

    b) How much potato salad did Neil's family eat?

    c) Each person ate the same amount of potato salad. How much potato salad did each person eat?

3. Students from two schools worked at a food bank. One school had 450 students. The other school had 360 students. Eight-tenths of the students in each school participated. How many more students participated from the school of 450 than the school of 360?

Communicate About Problem Solving

 Goal   **Explain how to solve problems involving decimal multiplication.**

1. Janice exercises for 360 min each week. She walks for 0.6 of the time, and rides her bicycle for the rest of the time.

   a) For how many minutes does Janice walk?

   b) For how many minutes does Janice ride her bicycle?

Choosing a Multiplication Method

 Goal Justify the choice of a multiplication method.

1. Multiply. Did you use mental math, pencil and paper, or a calculator?

   a) 0.6×5

   b) 1.8×9

   c) 0.52×4

   d) 0.37×100

   e) 2.9×4

   f) 5.7×100

   g) 0.04×100

   h) 0.8×7

2. Explain why you chose the method you did for three parts in Question 1.

Circle the correct answer.

1. Which estimate would be closest to the actual product? 8.3×21.20

   A. 8×21 **C.** 8×21 plus $\frac{1}{3}$ of 21

   B. 9×22 **D.** 9×24 plus $\frac{1}{3}$ of 24

2. Which is the best estimate for 0.8 kg at $28.95 per kilogram?

   A. $16   **B.** $18   **C.** $29   **D.** $32

3. What is the product of 1000 and 25.064?

   A. 250.64   **B.** 2506.4   **C.** 25 064   **D.** 250 640

4. What is the product of 0.891 and 1000?

   A. 8.91   **B.** 89.1   **C.** 891   **D.** 8910

5. What is 5.007 km in metres?

   A. 50 007 m   **B.** 50.07 m   **C.** 500.7 m   **D.** 5007 m

6. What is the product of 6.2 and 7?

   A. 42.2   **B.** 43.4   **C.** 44.4   **D.** 42.9

7. What is the product of 503 and 0.01?

   A. 0.503   **B.** 5.03   **C.** 50.3   **D.** 503

8. What is the product of 0.1 and 827?

   A. 8270   **B.** 827   **C.** 8.27   **D.** 82.7

9. One muffin has a mass of 0.025 kg. What is the mass in grams?

   A. 250 g   **B.** 0.25 g   **C.** 2.5 g   **D.** 25 g

10. What is the product of 0.4 and 3260?

    A. 652   **B.** 978   **C.** 1304   **D.** 1448

11. A library has 5460 books. Three-tenths of the books are mysteries. How many mystery books are there?

A. 546 books   **B.** 1638 books   **C.** 1820 books   **D.** 2730 books

12. Jason wants to multiply 0.6 by 920. He wrote

$0.1 \times 920 = \boxed{}$

$\boxed{} \times 92 = \boxed{}$

What are the missing numbers?

A. 92, 6, 552   **B.** 9.2, 6, 55.2   **C.** 92, 60, 5520   **D.** 92, 60, 552

13. Lina saved $240 planting trees. She spent 0.4 of that amount on a new jacket. How much did she spend on the jacket?

A. $60   **B.** $96   **C.** $120   **D.** $9.60

14. Which product is greatest?

A. 1000×0.6 **B.** 1000×0.105 **C.** 1000×0.92 **D.** 1000×0.033

15. Mitch bought 0.6 kg of grapes.
One kilogram cost $3.00 on sale.
The regular price was $4.00 per kilogram.
How much did Mitch save?

A. $1.80   **C.** $2.40

B. $0.80   **D.** $0.60

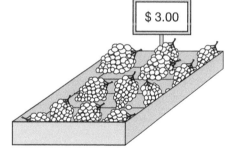

$ 3.00

Estimating Quotients

 Goal **Estimate quotients when dividing decimal numbers.**

1. Estimate each quotient. Show your work.

a) 8.4 ÷ 5

b) 13.7 ÷ 7

c) 18.3 ÷ 4

d) 24.2 ÷ 3

2. Ray bought 15.5 m of wire to make four sculptures with equal lengths of wire. Estimate the length of wire for each sculpture.

At–Home Help

To estimate a quotient when dividing a decimal number by a one-digit number, use one of these methods.
- Round the decimal number to the nearest whole number.

  For example: 5.9 ÷ 3
  Round 5.9 to 6.
  6 ÷ 3 = 2
  5.9 ÷ 3 is about 2.

- Rename the decimal number.

  For example: 2.8 ÷ 3
  2.8 is close to 2.7, which is an easier number to divide by 3.
  Rename 2.7 as 27 tenths.
  27 tenths ÷ 3 = 9 tenths, or 0.9
  2.8 ÷ 3 is about 0.9.

- Rewrite the division as a multiplication question.
  For example: 7.7 ÷ 6
  6 × □ = 7.7
  6 × 1.0 = 6.0
  6 × 1.1 = 6.6
  6 × 1.5 = 9.0

  7.7 ÷ 6 is between 1.1 and 1.5, or about 1.3.

Dividing Money

 Goal Solve problems by dividing money.

You will need a calculator.

1. Use a calculator to divide. Use multiplication to check your answers.

   a) $27.84 ÷ 3 = _____

   b) $36.85 ÷ 5 = _____

   c) $29.50 ÷ 2 = _____

   d) $45.96 ÷ 6 = _____

   e) $51.66 ÷ 7 = _____

2. Lara and two friends bought a book for $28.95, a pizza for $22.99, and a game for $26.85. Each person paid the same amount.

   a) What was the cost for each person? Use a calculator.

   b) Use estimation to show that your answer is reasonable.

Dividing Decimals by One-Digit Numbers

 Goal Express quotients as decimal numbers to tenths.

1. Divide. Check two answers using multiplication.

   a) 23.4 ÷ 3

   d) 6)37.2

   b) 30.4 ÷ 4

   e) 44.5 ÷ 5

   c) 7)41.3

   f) 8)25.6

2. Sheila has 3.0 kg of raisins. She keeps one-half for herself. She divides the remaining amount equally among three friends. How many kilograms of raisins does each person get? Show your work.

Dividing by 10, 100, 1000, and 10 000

 Goal Divide whole and decimal numbers by 10, 100, 1000, and 10 000 using mental math.

1. Calculate. Use mental math.

   a) 321 ÷ 100 = _____

   b) 25 ÷ 10 = _____

   c) 4.5 ÷ 10 = _____

   d) 321 ÷ 10 000 = _____

   e) 18 ÷ 1000 = _____

   f) 60.7 ÷ 100 = _____

   g) 58 240 ÷ 1000 = _____

   h) 58 240 ÷ 10 000 = _____

At-Home Help

To divide a decimal tenth by 10, 100, or 1000, move the digits to the right one, two, or three places.

For example,

   553 ÷ 10 = 55.3

   553 ÷ 100 = 5.53

   553 ÷ 1000 = 0.553

   553 ÷ 10 000 = 0.0553

   55.3 ÷ 10 = 5.53

   55.3 ÷ 100 = 0.553

   55.3 ÷ 1000 = 0.0553

   55.3 ÷ 10 000 = 0.005 33

2. Chris has 12.3 L of juice. He wants to pour equal amounts of juice into 10 glasses. How many litres of juice will be in each glass?

3. 56.2 kg of rice is divided equally into 100 containers. How many kilograms of rice are in each container?

4. Concert organizers ordered 3550 L of water for an audience of 10 000 people. How many millilitres of water will be available for each person?

Solving Problems by Working Backward

 Goal **Use a working-backward strategy to solve problems.**

Lynne has 17.2 m of ribbon to wrap two sizes of gifts. There are four small gifts and one larger gift. She needs 4.8 m to wrap the larger gift. How much ribbon does she need to wrap each smaller gift?

Test Yourself

Circle the correct answer.

1. Which quotient is the closest estimate for 14.6 ÷ 3?

   A. 4   **B.** 5   **C.** 6   **D.** 7

2. Miranda got 4.94 when she divided 34.58 by 7. Which method is incorrect to use to check her answer?

   A. Multiply 34.58 by 4.94.   **C.** Round 4.94 to 5. Then multiply by 7.

   B. Multiply 4.94 by 7.   **D.** Use a calculator to divide 34.58 by 7.

3. Which quotient answers the question $46.32 ÷ 4?

   A. $11.58   **B.** $11.98   **C.** $12.58   **D.** $12.98

4. Royce and four friends bought a book and a game. The book cost $16.99 and the game cost $24.96. Each paid the same amount. What was the cost for each person?

   A. $11.39   **B.** $10.75   **C.** $10.48   **D.** $8.39

5. Yvette paid $26.08 for eight different flags. Each flag cost the same amount. How much did each flag cost?

   A. $2.61   **B.** $3.00   **C.** $3.26   **D.** $3.50

6. What is the quotient of 67.2 ÷ 3?

   A. 21.8   **B.** 22.4   **C.** 24.3   **D.** 25.4

7. Nigel bought 4.5 kg of trail mix. He kept 2 kg for himself. He divided the remaining amount equally among five friends. How many kilograms of trail mix did each friend get?

   A. 0.3 kg   **B.** 0.4 kg   **C.** 0.5 kg   **D.** 0.6 kg

8. Which quotient is incorrect?

   A. 40.3 ÷ 10 = 4.03   **C.** 3.5 ÷ 100 = 0.35

   B. 690 ÷ 1000 = 0.69   **D.** 7 ÷ 1000 = 0.007

9. 20.4 L of fruit punch is divided equally into 100 containers. How many litres of punch are in each container?

   A. 204 L   **B.** 2.04 L   **C.** 0.204 L   **D.** 0.024 L

10. Nemil added 0.6 years to his age, and divided that result by 4. The final answer was 2.4. How old is Nemil?

    A. 8   **B.** 9   **C.** 10   **D.** 11

Visualizing and Constructing Polyhedrons

 Goal **Visualize and build polyhedrons from 2-D nets.**

A.

B.

C.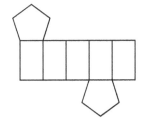

D.

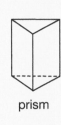
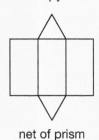
1. Which are nets of pyramids? How can you tell?

2. Which are nets of prisms? How can you tell?

3. What nets can you make from these shapes? Sketch each net and name the polyhedron it would make.

Surface Area of Polyhedrons

Determine the surface area of triangular and rectangular prisms.

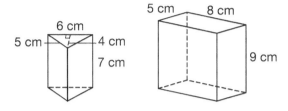

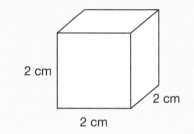

At–Home Help

The **surface area** of a polyhedron is the total area of all of the faces, or surfaces, of that polyhedron.

For example, the surface area of this cube is 24 cm² because each face has an area of 4 cm².

1. **a)** Sketch a net for the triangular prism. Label the dimensions.

   b) Determine the surface area of the triangular prism.

2. **a)** Sketch a net for the rectangular prism. Label the dimensions.

   b) Determine the surface area of the rectangular prism.

Volume of Rectangular and Triangular Prisms

 Goal   Calculate the volume of rectangular and triangular prisms.

1. Determine the volume of each rectangular prism.

a)
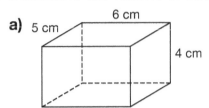

b)
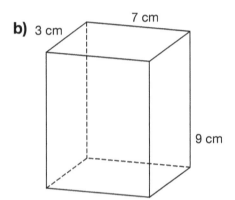

2. Determine the volume of each triangular prism.

a)
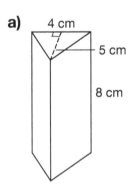

b)
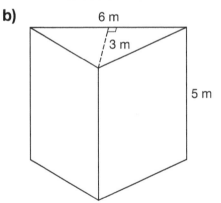

At-Home Help

Volume is the amount of space an object takes up.

You can calculate the volume of a prism using the rule
Volume = area of base × height.

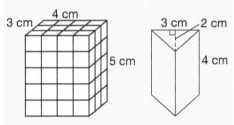

Volume of rectangular prism
= area of base × height
= (length × width) × height
= (4 cm × 3 cm) × 5 cm
= 12 cm² × 5 cm
= 60 cm³

Volume of triangular prism
= area of base × height
= (3 cm × 2 cm ÷ 2) × 4 cm
= 3 cm² × 4 cm
= 12 cm³

Solve Problems by Making a Model

 Goal **Make models to solve problems.**

You will need centimetre cubes.

1. Jared is building rectangular prisms with 12 centimetre cubes.

   a) Which prism has the least surface area?

   b) What is the volume of the prism in part **a)**?

Creating Isometric Sketches

 Sketch a polyhedron built from cubes.

a)

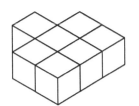

c)

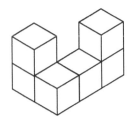

b)

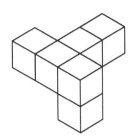

d)

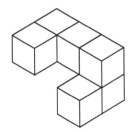

At-Home Help

An **isometric drawing** is a three-dimensional view of an object that can be drawn on isometric dot paper. All equal lengths on the cubes are equal on the grid.

For example, the vertices of this cube are placed on the dots.

1. Sketch each structure.

a)

c)

b)

d)

Creating Cube Structures from Sketches

Goal Create cube structures based on an isometric sketch.

You will need linking cubes or other cube-shaped objects for building.

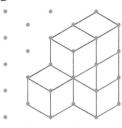

1. **a)** Build a cube structure based on the isometric drawing. How many cubes did you use?

   _____ cubes

   b) Sketch at least two views of your cube structure so someone else could build it exactly as you did.

At-Home Help

It is possible to build cube structures based on isometric drawings.

For example, the isometric drawings below represent a cube structure.

Two cube structures that match the drawing would be

In order to know exactly how many cubes to use, you need more than one drawing to show what the cube structure looks like.

2. **a)** Build another cube structure using more cubes than you used in Question 1.

   How many cubes did you use? _____ cubes

   b) Sketch at least two views of your cube structure so someone else could build it exactly as you did.

Different Views of a Cube Structure

 Goal Draw top, front, and side views of a cube structure.

1. Sketch the top, front, right, and left views of this cube structure.

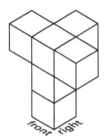

At-Home Help

Cube structures can be represented accurately if their top, front, and side views are shown.

For example, the cube structure above can be represented by top, front, and side views.

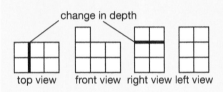

2. **a)** Sketch the top, front, right, and left views of this cube structure.

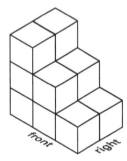

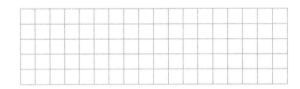

   b) Why is it important to include both side views?

Creating Cube Structures from Different Views

Goal **Make cube structures when given their top, front, and side views.**

You will need linking cubes or other cube-shaped objects for building.

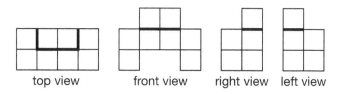

top view   front view   right view   left view

1. **a)** Make three different cube structures that match the top view.

   b) Make three different cube structures that match the right view. Do any of your cube structures match both the top and right views?

   c) Make several different cube structures that match the front view. Do any of your cube structures match all four views?

At–Home Help

A cube structure can be constructed when its top, front, and side views are given.

For example, if you are given these views, you can build the appropriate cube structure.

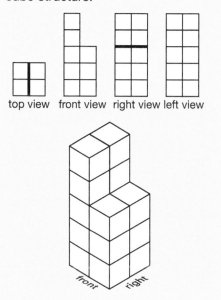

top view   front view   right view   left view

Test Yourself   Page 1

Circle the correct answer.

Use the polygons below to answer Questions 1 and 2.

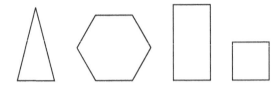

1. Which combination of shapes would make a pyramid?

   A. 3 triangles, 1 square   **C.** 5 triangles, 1 hexagon

   B. 4 triangles, 1 rectangle   **D.** 6 triangles, 1 hexagon

2. Which combination of shapes would *not* make a prism?

   A. 2 hexagons, 3 rectangles, 3 squares   **C.** 2 triangles, 3 rectangles

   B. 2 hexagons, 6 rectangles   **D.** 2 triangles, 3 squares

Use the prism below to answer Questions 3 and 4.

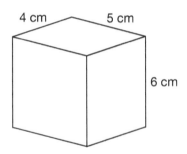

3. What is the surface area of the rectangular prism?

   A. 74 cm^2 **B.** 120 cm^2 **C.** 148 cm^2 **D.** 240 cm^2

4. What is the volume of the rectangular prism?

   A. 74 cm^3 **B.** 120 cm^3 **C.** 148 cm^3 **D.** 240 cm^3

Test Yourself   Page 2

Use the prism below to answer Questions 5 and 6.

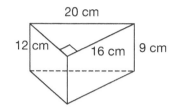

5. What is the surface area of the triangular prism?

   A. 624 cm^2 **B.** 424 cm^2 **C.** 570 cm^2 **D.** 1040 cm^2

6. What is the volume of the triangular prism?

   A. 960 cm^3 **B.** 2800 cm^3 **C.** 864 cm^3 **D.** 2240 cm^3

7. All of the cube structures below are made with seven cubes. Which ones are the same?

a
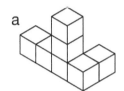
c
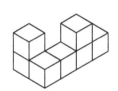
e
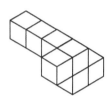

b
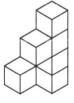
d

f
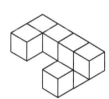

   A. a, d   **B.** b, c   **C.** b, e   **D.** a, f

8. Which top, front, and side views match cube structure c in Question 7?

A.

top view   front view   side view

C.

top view

front view

side view

B.
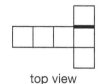
top view   front view   side view

D.
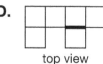
top view

front view   side view

Comparing and Ordering Fractions

 Goal **Compare and order fractions on number lines.**

1. Compare. Write >, <, or =.

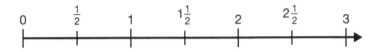

a) $\dfrac{4}{3}$ ☐ $\dfrac{2}{3}$

b) $\dfrac{2}{5}$ ☐ $\dfrac{4}{10}$

c) $\dfrac{7}{4}$ ☐ $\dfrac{3}{8}$

d) $1\dfrac{1}{3}$ ☐ $1\dfrac{4}{6}$

e) $1\dfrac{3}{4}$ ☐ $2\dfrac{1}{2}$

f) $2\dfrac{1}{5}$ ☐ $2\dfrac{1}{10}$

2. Order each set of numbers from least to greatest. Use a number line.

a) $\dfrac{3}{8}$, $1\dfrac{1}{4}$, $\dfrac{3}{4}$, $\dfrac{5}{8}$

b) $2\dfrac{1}{3}$, $1\dfrac{2}{3}$, $\dfrac{8}{3}$, $1\dfrac{3}{6}$

c) $\dfrac{4}{4}$, $1\dfrac{1}{8}$, $\dfrac{2}{4}$, $\dfrac{7}{4}$, $1\dfrac{5}{8}$

d) $\dfrac{5}{6}$, $\dfrac{2}{3}$, $\dfrac{1}{6}$, $1\dfrac{1}{3}$, $\dfrac{6}{3}$

At–Home Help

To compare fractions, use a number line to mark the positions of the fractions.

The order of the fractions can be read from the number line. For example, to order $\dfrac{3}{4}$, $\dfrac{3}{8}$, and $\dfrac{2}{3}$, use a number line.

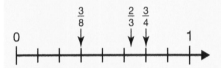

The order from least to greatest is $\dfrac{3}{8}$, $\dfrac{2}{3}$, and $\dfrac{3}{4}$.

Comparing Fractions with Unlike Denominators

Goal Compare fractions when the denominators are different.

1. Compare. Write >, <, or =.

   a) $\frac{1}{3}$ ☐ $\frac{4}{5}$ **d)** $\frac{3}{4}$ ☐ $\frac{2}{3}$

   b) $\frac{2}{5}$ ☐ $\frac{1}{2}$ **e)** $\frac{6}{10}$ ☐ $\frac{3}{5}$

   c) $\frac{3}{8}$ ☐ $\frac{1}{3}$ **f)** $1\frac{1}{2}$ ☐ $\frac{5}{8}$

2. Which amount is greater? Tell how you know.

   a) $\frac{1}{3}$ or $\frac{3}{8}$ of a bag of popcorn

   b) $\frac{2}{5}$ or $\frac{2}{3}$ of a container of juice

   c) $\frac{5}{7}$ or $\frac{1}{2}$ of a length of string

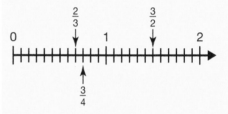

Fraction and Decimal Equivalents

 Goal Relate fractions to decimals and determine equivalents.

1. Write an equivalent fraction for each decimal.

   a) 0.34 = _____

   b) 0.6 = _____

   c) 0.07 = _____

   d) 1.3 = _____

   e) 2.37 = _____

   f) 3.04 = _____

2. Explain how to write $\frac{4}{5}$ as a decimal.

Ratios

 Goal Identify and model ratios to describe situations.

1. Write the ratio of grey items to white items.

   a)

   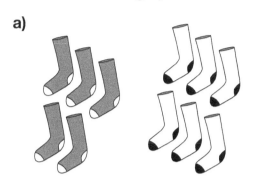

...

At-Home Help

A **ratio** is a comparison of two numbers or quantities measured in the same units.

If you mix juice using 1 can of concentrate and 3 cans of water, the ratio of concentrate to water is 1 : 3, or 1 to 3.

   b)

   c)   **d)**

2. Write the ratio of white to grey for each situation in Question 1.

   a)   **b)**   **c)**   **d)**

3. **a)** What is the ratio of oats to raisins?

   b) What is the ratio of coconut to oats?

   ```
   3 parts oats

   1 part coconut

   2 parts raisins
   ```

   c) What is the ratio of raisins to coconut?

Equivalent Ratios

 Goal   Determine equivalent ratios and use them to solve problems.

1. Determine the missing number to make an equivalent ratio.

   a) 5 to 8 = ☐ to 16

   b) 12 : 100 = 3 : ☐

   c) 21 to ☐ = 7 to 11

   d) 18 : 6 = ☐ : 3

   e) 75 : ☐ = 25 : 8

   f) 24 to 60 = ☐ to 5

2. Kenton makes salsa by mixing tomatoes and peppers in a ratio of 5 to 2.

   a) Write ratios equivalent to 5 : 2 in the ratio table.

Tomatoes	5		15			30
Peppers	2	4		8	10	

   b) If Kenton has 40 tomatoes, how many peppers does he need?

   c) If Kenton has 20 peppers, how many tomatoes does he need?

3. Stacy makes one batch of muffins using muffin mix and water in a ratio of 3 : 1. She needs to make 4 batches for school. How many cups of muffin mix will she need?

Percents as Special Ratios

 Goal **Understand the meaning of percent.**

1. Write each as a ratio, a fraction, and a percent.

   a) 10 to 25

   c) 13 out of 20

   b) 0.07

   d) 0.18

2. Write each ratio as an equivalent fraction with a denominator of 100, a decimal, and a percent.

   a) $\frac{9}{20}$ —

   b) $\frac{33}{50}$

   c) 2 out of 5

   d) 8 out of 25

3. A survey at Jennifer's school showed that 19 out of 25 students chose pizza as their favourite lunch food.

   a) What percent of students chose pizza?

   b) What percent of students did not choose pizza?

Relating Percents to Decimals and Fractions

 Goal **Compare and order percents, fractions, and decimals.**

1. Write each number as a percent. Order the numbers from least to greatest.

   a) 0.6, $\frac{7}{10}$, 0.07, $\frac{8}{20}$

   b) $\frac{4}{5}$, 0.12, $\frac{16}{25}$, 0.85

2. An art show has paintings, sculptures, and sketches. Thirty-five percent of the items are paintings and 0.13 of the items are sketches. What fraction of the items are sculptures?

Estimating and Calculating Percents

Goal **Estimate and calculate percents.**

1. Estimate the percent of each number.
   Show your work.

   a) 40% of 180

   b) 30% of 90

   c) 50% of 412

   d) 75% of 208

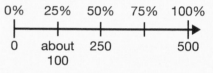

At–Home Help

To estimate the percent of a number, use benchmarks such as 10%, 25%, 50%, and 75%.

10% is the same as $\frac{1}{10}$.

25% is the same as $\frac{1}{4}$.

50% is the same as $\frac{1}{2}$.

75% is the same as $\frac{3}{4}$.

100% is the same as 1 whole.

For example, to estimate 25% of 500 km, use a number line.

```
0%    25%   50%   75%  100%
├──────┼─────┼─────┼─────►
0    about  250         500
     100
```

50% of 500 km is half of 500 or 250 km.

So 25% is half of 250 km or about 100 km.

2. A store has a sign saying, "15% off all jackets." Kenny wants to buy a leather jacket that has a regular price of $360. About how much will Kenny save?

Unit Rates

Goal   **Represent relationships using unit rates.**

1. Calculate the unit rate for each item.

   a) 5 guitar picks for $1.00

> **At–Home Help**
>
> A **unit rate** is a comparison of two quantities where the second one is described as one unit.
>
> For example, a unit rate might be 30 km in 1 h or 4 tomatoes for $1.00.
>
> Rates often have words like "per" or "for" in them. A slash (/) is sometimes used instead.
>
> For example, you read 100 km/h as "100 km per hour."

   b) 2 CDs for $15.00

   c) 8 mini-muffins for $2.40

   d) 3 tickets for $3.00

2. **a)** What is the price of one scoop of each type of ice cream?

> **Ice cream**
>
> Vanilla
> 3 scoops for $1.50
>
> Chocolate
> 2 scoops for $1.40
>
> Mango
> 4 scoops for $4.00
>
> Strawberry
> 4 scoops for $3.60

   b) Which ice cream is the least expensive?

   c) Which ice cream is the most expensive?

Solving Problems Using Guess and Test

 Goal **Use a guess and test strategy to solve problems.**

The ratio of flowers to herbs in Babak's garden is 6 : 2. He started with 80 plants. He wants to increase the number of herbs in his garden so that 40% of his plants are herbs. How many more herb plants must he get?

At-Home Help

Sometimes using a guess and test strategy is a good way to solve a problem.

Use a chart to help you organize the information you are given and what you want to calculate.

Remember to check if your answer is reasonable after guessing.

Test Yourself   Page 1

Circle the correct answer.

1. Which fraction is greatest?

   $\frac{4}{5}, \frac{2}{3}, \frac{3}{4}, \frac{3}{8}$

   A. $\frac{4}{5}$ **B.** $\frac{2}{3}$ **C.** $\frac{3}{4}$ **D.** $\frac{3}{8}$

2. What is the correct order of these fractions from least to greatest?

   $\frac{2}{3}, \frac{1}{6}, 1\frac{1}{5}, \frac{7}{8}, \frac{2}{5}$

   A. $\frac{2}{5}, \frac{2}{3}, \frac{1}{6}, \frac{7}{8}, 1\frac{1}{5}$ **C.** $\frac{1}{6}, \frac{2}{3}, \frac{2}{5}, \frac{7}{8}, 1\frac{1}{5}$

   B. $\frac{1}{6}, \frac{2}{5}, \frac{2}{3}, \frac{7}{8}, 1\frac{1}{5}$ **D.** $\frac{2}{3}, \frac{2}{5}, \frac{1}{6}, \frac{7}{8}, 1\frac{1}{5}$

3. What is 1.03 as a fraction?

   A. $\frac{13}{100}$ **B.** $1\frac{3}{10}$ **C.** $1\frac{3}{100}$ **D.** $\frac{103}{1000}$

4. What is the ratio of white counters to grey counters?

   A. 4 : 3   **C.** 4 : 7

   B. 3 : 7   **D.** 3 : 4

5. Which ratios are equivalent to 6 out of 15?

   i) 2 : 5   ii) 3 out of 10   iii) 4 out of 10   iv) 10 : 25   v) 20 : 45

   A. i, ii, iii   **B.** ii, iv, v   **C.** i, iii, iv   **D.** ii, iii, iv

6. What is the correct order of these numbers from least to greatest?

   $\frac{8}{25}, 0.14, 30\%, \frac{2}{5}, 8\%, 0.09$

   A. $8\%, 0.09, 0.14, 30\%, \frac{8}{25}, \frac{2}{5}$ **C.** $0.09, \frac{2}{5}, 0.14, \frac{8}{25}, 8\%, 30\%$

   B. $0.09, 0.14, \frac{2}{5}, \frac{8}{25}, 8\%, 30\%$ **D.** $8\%, 0.09, \frac{2}{5}, 0.14, \frac{8}{25}, 30\%$

7. What is 0.3 as a ratio, a fraction, and a percent?

   A. $3 : 100$, $\dfrac{3}{100}$, 30%

   B. $3 : 10$, $\dfrac{3}{10}$, 30%

   C. $3 : 10$, $\dfrac{3}{10}$, 3%

   D. $3 : 10$, $\dfrac{3}{100}$, 3%

8. What is $\dfrac{12}{25}$ as an equivalent fraction with a denominator of 100, a decimal, and a percent?

   A. $\dfrac{12}{100}$, 0.12, 12%

   B. $\dfrac{40}{100}$, 0.4, 40%

   C. $\dfrac{48}{100}$, 0.48, 48%

   D. $\dfrac{16}{100}$, 0.16, 16%

9. What is the best estimate for 25% of 212?

   A. about 30   **B.** about 40   **C.** about 50   **D.** about 60

10. Which type of muffin is the least expensive?

    A. cinnamon raisin

    B. maple pecan

    C. cranberry orange

    D. crunchy oat

Muffins
Blueberry bran . . . . . 5 for $3.50
Cranberry orange . . . 6 for $3.60
Crunchy oat . . . . 8 for $3.20
Maple pecan . . . . . . 3 for $2.70
Cinnamon raisin . . . . 5 for $2.50

11. A brand of light cheese says "20% less fat" on the label. The regular version of the cheese has 85 g of fat. About how many fewer grams of fat are in the light cheese?

    A. about 10 g   **B.** about 20 g   **C.** about 30 g   **D.** about 40 g

Conducting Probability Experiments

 Goal **Compare probabilities in two experiments.**

Game 1
1. Place a shuffled deck of cards face down.
2. Turn over the top card.
3. If the card is an ace, you get 4 points.
A player wins if he or she has at least 10 points after 4 turns.

Game 2
1. Place a shuffled deck of cards face down.
2. Turn over the top card.
3. If the card is a red card (heart or diamond), you get 2 points.
A player wins if she or he has at least 6 points after 4 turns.

1. Predict which game you are more likely to win. Justify your prediction.

2. Tammy played both games three times.
   Which game are you more likely to win? Use probability language to explain why.

Game 1   Points

Turn number	1	2	3	4	
Ace?	×	×	×	✓	4
Turn number	1	2	3	4	
Ace?	×	×	✓	×	4
Turn number	1	2	3	4	
Ace?	×	×	×	×	0

Game 2   Points

Turn number	1	2	3	4	
Red card?	✓	✓	×	✓	6
Turn number	1	2	3	4	
Red card?	×	✓	✓	✓	6
Turn number	1	2	3	4	
Red card?	✓	×	✓	✓	6

Using Percents to Describe Probabilities

 Goal **Conduct experiments and use percent to describe probabilities.**

1. Siegfried rolled a die 20 times.

Roll	1	2	3	4	5	6	7	8	9	10
Number on die	2	3	1	4	2	6	3	5	2	1
Roll	11	12	13	14	15	16	17	18	19	20
Number on die	5	3	1	2	6	4	1	3	2	4

Record the probability of each event as a percent.

a) rolling a 1

c) rolling an odd number

b) rolling a multiple of 3   **d)** rolling a 7

At–Home Help

Probabilities can be written as percents.

For example, if you rolled a die 10 times and got a 4 three times, the probability of rolling a 4 would be 3 out of 10, or $\frac{3}{10}$.

To express $\frac{3}{10}$ as a percent, find an equivalent fraction.

$\frac{3}{10} = \frac{30}{100}$

$\phantom{\frac{3}{10}} = 30\%$

2. The probability of winning a game is 40%. Predict how many times you expect to win in each situation.

a) if you play 10 times   **b)** if you play 25 times   **c)** if you play 50 times

3. **a)** Roll a die 25 times and record each roll.

Roll	1	2	3	4	5	6	7	8	9	10	11	12	13	14	15	16	17	18	19	20	21	22	23	24	25
Number on die																									

b) Record each probability as a percent.

i) rolling an even number   **ii)** rolling a number less than 5   **iii)** rolling a number less than 10

Solving a Problem by Conducting an Experiment

 Goal Use an experiment as a problem solving strategy.

Jessica and her brother use a die to decide who will help with dinner each night. An even number means it is Jessica's turn. An odd number means it is her brother's turn. Conduct an experiment to determine the probability that Jessica will help with dinner more than 3 times in the next week.

Theoretical Probability

 Goal Create a list of all possible outcomes to determine a probability.

1. If you shuffle a deck of cards, what is the theoretical probability of each event?

   a) picking an ace

   b) picking a spade

   c) picking a face card

> ### At–Home Help
>
> **Theoretical probability** is the probability you would expect when you analyze all of the different possible outcomes.
>
> For example, the theoretical probability of flipping a head on a coin is $\frac{1}{2}$, since there are 2 equally likely outcomes and only 1 is favourable.
>
> Experimental probability is the probability that actually happens when you do the experiment.

2. If you roll a die two times, what is the theoretical probability of each event?

   a) sum of 6

Roll 1

Roll 2	1	2	3	4	5	6
1						
2						
3						
4						
5						
6						

   b) sum of 10

   c) difference of 5

Roll 1

Roll 2	1	2	3	4	5	6
1						
2						
3						
4						
5						
6						

   d) difference of 2

3. Imagine spinning this spinner twice.

   a) What is the theoretical probability that the sum of the two spins is greater than 4?

   b) What is the theoretical probability that the sum is an odd number?

Tree Diagrams

Goal Use a tree diagram to determine a theoretical probability.

1. **a)** Use a tree diagram to list the possible outcomes if this spinner is spun twice.

b) Determine the theoretical probability that the difference of the numbers is 0.

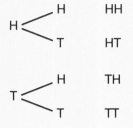
c) Determine the theoretical probability that the product of the numbers is greater than 6.

2. Nathan and Jay are playing a game with the spinner in Question 1. Nathan wins if his two spins give a sum greater than 5. Otherwise, Jay wins. Use a tree diagram to explain if this game is fair.

Comparing Theoretical and Experimental Probability

 Goal **Compare the theoretical probability of an event with the results of an experiment.**

1. Two green marbles, two blue marbles, and one yellow marble are placed in a bag. The marbles are mixed up and two marbles are picked, one at a time, without looking.

   a) What is the theoretical probability of picking a green marble and then a yellow one? Use a tree diagram.

At-Home Help

To determine the theoretical probability of an event, you can use a tree diagram to list all possible outcomes.

To determine the experimental probability of that event, conduct an experiment.

Before comparing theoretical and experimental probabilities, make sure the experiment was conducted many times.

Usually experimental probabilities are not the same as theoretical probabilities. If you do a great enough number of experiments, the experimental probability will be the same as or very close to the theoretical one.

   b) Conduct an experiment 20 times. What is your experimental probability for this event? Record your results beside your tree diagram in part **a)**.

   c) Why might the experimental probability be different from the theoretical probability?

Test Yourself   Page 1

Circle the correct answer.

Use the chart to answer Questions 1 and 2.

Nazir's Rolls of a Die

First 5 rolls	2	1	6	3	5
Next 5 rolls	1	1	4	2	5
Next 5 rolls	3	2	4	5	1

1. What is the probability of Nazir rolling an even number in the first 10 rolls?

   A. $\frac{3}{10}$ **B.** $\frac{4}{10}$ **C.** $\frac{7}{10}$ **D.** $\frac{3}{5}$

2. What is the probability of Nazir rolling a number greater than 4 in all 15 rolls?

   A. $\frac{4}{15}$ **B.** $\frac{1}{3}$ **C.** $\frac{7}{15}$ **D.** $\frac{11}{15}$

3. What is the theoretical probability of spinning blue on this spinner?

   A. $\frac{1}{6}$ **C.** $\frac{2}{3}$

   B. $\frac{2}{6}$ **D.** $\frac{1}{2}$

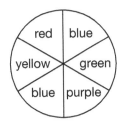

4. Renata spun the spinner in Question 3 10 times. What is the probability of Renata spinning blue?

Spin number	1	2	3	4	5	6	7	8	9	10
Colour	blue	yellow	green	red	green	green	purple	blue	blue	red

   A. 10%   **B.** 20%   **C.** 30%   **D.** 40%

5. What is the theoretical probability of flipping a coin three times and getting heads all three times?

   A. $\frac{1}{8}$ **B.** $\frac{1}{4}$ **C.** $\frac{3}{8}$ **D.** $\frac{1}{2}$

6. What is the theoretical probability of picking an ace from a shuffled deck of cards?

   A. $\frac{1}{52}$ **B.** $\frac{4}{52}$ **C.** $\frac{1}{2}$ **D.** $\frac{3}{4}$

7. One red counter, one blue counter, one green counter, and one yellow counter are placed in a bag. The counters are mixed up and two counters are picked, one at a time, without looking. Each time a counter is picked, it is not replaced in the bag. Which tree diagram represents all possible outcomes?

A.

C.

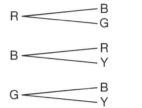

B.

D.

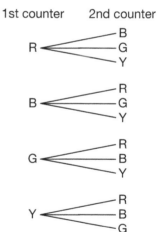

8. What is the theoretical probability of picking a green counter and a yellow counter (in any order) for the situation in Question 7?

   A. $\frac{1}{12}$ **B.** $\frac{2}{12}$ **C.** $\frac{1}{4}$ **D.** $\frac{1}{3}$

Describing Rotations

Goal   **Perform and describe the rotation of a shape around a centre that is on the shape.**

You will need a ruler and a protractor.

1. Describe the rotation of this shape.

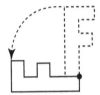

At–Home Help

A **rotation** is a turn of a shape. A rotation is described by the centre of rotation, the angle of rotation, and the direction of the turn.

The **centre of rotation** is the point that a shape rotates around. Each point in the shape must stay an equal distance from the centre of rotation.

The **angle of rotation** is how much the shape moved about the centre of rotation. The direction of rotation can be described as clockwise (CW) or counterclockwise (CCW).

For example, the shape below is rotated 90° CW about vertex A.

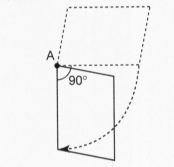

2. **a)** Describe how to rotate the letter so that it ends up in the same position.

    b) Describe a rotation that will change how the letter looks. Sketch the rotation.

3. Rotate the letter 90° CW several times. What do you notice about the results?

Performing and Measuring Rotations

 Goal   **Perform and describe rotations of shapes about centres not on the shape.**

You will need a ruler, scissors, and a protractor.

1. Describe each rotation. Include the centre of rotation, angle, and direction.

   a)

   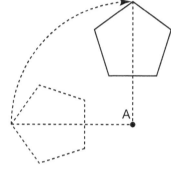

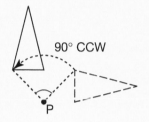
   b)

   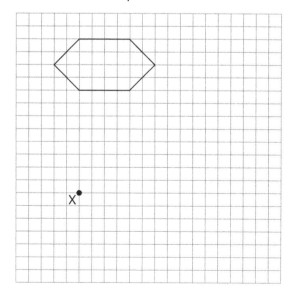

2. Trace the hexagon and cut it out. Rotate the hexagon 90° CW about point X. Sketch the final position.

Rotational Symmetry

 Goal **Determine whether and how a shape can be turned to fit on itself.**

1. **a)** Predict the order of rotational symmetry for this shape.

b) Trace and cut out the shape. Determine the order of rotational symmetry.

2. Name each shape.
   List its order of rotational symmetry.

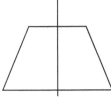

_____

_____

_____

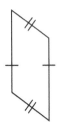

_____

_____

Communicate Using Diagrams

 Goal Use clear, labelled diagrams to communicate.

You will need a ruler and a protractor.

1. **a)** Melanie said that if you reflect shape K in
   the line of reflection A, then in the line of
   reflection B, then in the line of reflection A,
   then in the line of reflection B, you get the
   same shape you started with. Draw a diagram
   to check Melanie's prediction. Use the
   Communication Checklist.

At-Home Help

A clear, labelled diagram can be
used to communicate information.

If you are showing a rotation,
mark the centre of rotation, the
angle of rotation, and the direction
of rotation.

Use the Communication Checklist.

Communication Checklist
☑ Is your diagram easy to
   understand?
☑ Did you include measurements for
   all important sides and angles?
☑ Did you use a general enough
   example or use many examples?
☑ Did you give enough information?

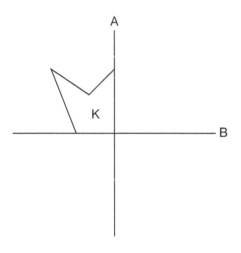

b) What other transformations could you perform on shape K to get the same shape
   you started with? Draw a diagram to show your transformation(s).

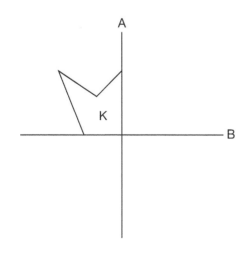

Exploring Transformation Patterns with Technology

Goal Relate number patterns to translation, rotation, and reflection patterns.

You will need a ruler.

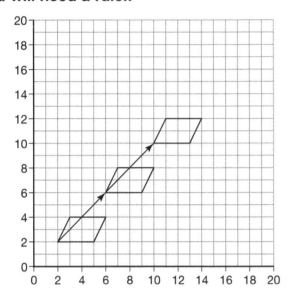

1. **a)** Describe the pattern for the bottom left vertex if the translations continue the same way.

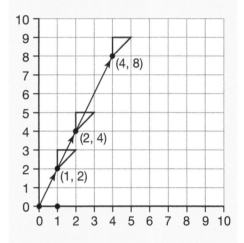
b) What would be the 10th term in the pattern?

Creating Designs

Goal Create a design by performing transformations on a basic shape.

You will need scissors and a protractor.

1. **a)** Trace this shape and cut it out. Create a design by transforming this shape. Use translations, reflections, or rotations.

b) Describe the transformations you used.

c) Can you get the same design by doing different transformations?

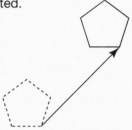
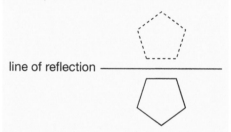
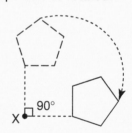
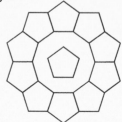

Test Yourself   Page 1

Circle the correct answer.

1. What is the best description of this rotation?

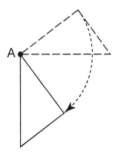

   A. The triangle is rotated 90° CW.

   B. The centre of rotation is A and the angle of rotation is 90°.

   C. The triangle is rotated 90° CW about A.

   D. The triangle is rotated 90° CCW about A.

2. What is the best description of this rotation?

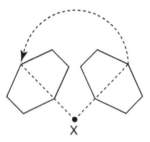

   A. The shape is rotated 90° CW.

   B. The centre of rotation is X and the angle of rotation is 90°.

   C. The shape is rotated 90° CW about X.

   D. The shape is rotated 90° CCW about X.

3. What is the order of rotational symmetry of this regular pentagon?

   A. 3   **B.** 4   **C.** 5   **D.** 6

4. Which shape has no rotational symmetry?

A. equilateral triangle

B. square

C. kite

D. regular hexagon

5. What will be the 10th figure in this pattern?

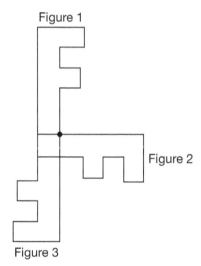

Figure 1

Figure 2

Figure 3

A.

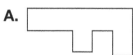

B.

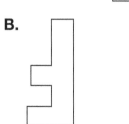

C.

D.

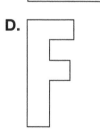

Page 1

Writing Pattern Rules

Goal Use rules to extend patterns and write pattern rules.

1. Steve learned that a year on Venus is about seven Earth months long.

a) Complete the table for Venus.

Venus	
Number of years on Venus	**Number of months on Earth**
1	7
2	14
3	21
4	28

b) Write a pattern rule to calculate the number of Earth months in any number of years on Venus.

Multiply 7 by the term number.

c) Use your pattern rule to calculate the approximate number of Earth months in 12 years on Venus.

about 84 months
7 × 12 = 84

2. Bev saves $12 each month from her paper route.

a) Write a pattern of numbers that shows the amount Bev saves in 1 to 4 months.

Number of months	Amount
1	$12
2	$24
3	$36
4	$48

b) Write a pattern rule to calculate the amount she saves in any number of months.

Multiply $12 by the term number.

c) Use your pattern rule to calculate the amount Bev saves in 10 months.

$12 × 10 = $120

d) Bev wants to buy a new hockey jersey for $100. For how many months does she need to save?

about 9 months $12 × 9 = $108
Bev will have $108 after 9 months.

Page 2

Relationship Rules for Patterns

Goal Write relationship pattern rules based on the term number.

1.

design 1   design 2   design 3   design 4

a) Complete the table to show the number of dots in designs 1 to 4.

Design number	Number of dots
1	2
2	5
3	8
4	11

b) Write the first term and the common difference.

The first term is 2. The common difference is 3.

c) How many dots are in design 8?

23 dots
8th term = 2 + seven 3s
= 2 + 21
= 23

2. Determine the 11th term in each pattern. Use a pattern rule. Show your work.

a) 1, 5, 9, 13, ...
The first term is 1. The common difference is 4.
11th term = 1 + ten 4s
= 1 + 40
= 41

b) 21, 26, 31, 36, ...
The first term is 21. The common difference is 5.
11th term = 21 + ten 5s
= 21 + 50
= 71

c) 2.2, 4.4, 6.6, 8.8, ...
The first term is 2.2. The common difference is 2.2.
11th term = 2.2 + ten 2.2s
= 2.2 + 22
= 24.2

d) $1.25, $1.75, $2.25, $2.75, ...
The first term is $1.25. The common difference is $0.50. 11th term = $1.25 + ten $0.50s
= $1.25 + $5.00
= $6.25

Variables in Expressions

Goal Use variables in an expression.

1. Arpita is baking cookies for a school bake sale.
One batch of cookies uses 75 g of chocolate chips.

a) Calculate the number of grams of chocolate
chips in the first four batches of cookies.

Suggested answer:

Batch number	Number of grams of chocolate chips
1	75
2	150
3	225
4	300

b) Write an explicit pattern rule for the number
of grams of chocolate chips in the 10th batch.

10th term = 75 × 10

c) Write your pattern rule using a variable for the
batch number. Use the variable b.

75 × b

d) Calculate the number of grams of chocolate chips in the first four batches using
your answer in part c). Show your work.

Suggested answer: for b = 1, 75 × 1 = 75 g
for b = 2, 75 × 2 = 150 g
for b = 3, 75 × 3 = 225 g
for b = 4, 75 × 4 = 300 g

e) How many grams of chocolate chips does Arpita need to make 11 batches
of cookies?

825 g
Suggested answer: for b = 11, 75 × 11 = 825

At-Home Help

A **variable** is a letter or symbol that
is used to show a quantity. This
quantity can have different values.

For example, t is a variable that could
be used to represent the amount of
time you surf the Internet each day.

Variables are usually used when
writing explicit pattern rules to
make the rules easier to write.

For example, an explicit pattern rule
for the pattern 50, 100, 150, 200, …
is 50 × n. The variable n is the
term number.

Term (n)	Value (50 × n)
1	50 × 1 = 50
2	50 × 2 = 100
3	50 × 3 = 150

Representing Patterns on a Graph

Goal Represent patterns in tables and on graphs.

1. George buys baseballs in packages of 6.

a) Complete the table to show the total number of
baseballs in 0 to 6 packages.

Number of packages	Number of baseballs
0	0
1	6
2	12
3	18
4	24
5	30
6	36

b) Graph the number of baseballs compared to
the number of packages.

Number of Baseballs Compared to
Number of Packages

c) Write a pattern rule to calculate the number of
baseballs in any number of packages. Use the
variable n in your rule.

6 × n

d) Determine the number of baseballs in 15 packages.

6 × 15 = 90
There are 90 baseballs in 15 packages.

At-Home Help

Patterns can be represented in tables
or graphs.

For example: It costs $2.50 to buy a
package of juice boxes. To determine
the cost of 20 packages, you can
extend a table or graph, or use a
pattern rule.

Number of packages	Cost
0	0
1	$2.50
2	$5.00
3	$7.50
4	$10.00
5	$12.50

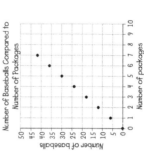

Cost Compared to Number
of Packages

A pattern rule to calculate the cost
for any number of packages is
$2.50 × n.

Cost of 20 packages = $2.50 × 20
= $50.00

Patterns and Spreadsheets

Goal Create patterns using spreadsheets and compare the growth.

Pamela wants to know how much money she would have if her bank tripled her money every day for 30 days. She starts with $2.

1. Complete the table or spreadsheet to show a pattern for Pamela's money. *Suggested answer:*

	A	B
1	Day number	Amount
2	1	$2
3	2	$6
4	3	$18
5	4	$54

2. What is the formula for calculating the amount on day 4?
Suggested answer: amount = 3 × $18 or B5 = 3*B4

3. **a)** Predict the amount Pamela would have on day 14.
Suggested answer:
I predict that she would have $1 000 000.

b) Calculate the amount on day 14.
$3 188 646

c) How close was your prediction?
Suggested answer: My prediction was too low. Pamela would get over $3 000 000 on day 14.

4. Describe the pattern in the amounts Pamela would have.
Suggested answer: The first term in the pattern is $2. This pattern does not have a common difference. To get any term in the pattern, you have to multiply the term before it by 3.

At-Home Help

Patterns can be represented using a spreadsheet. A **spreadsheet** is a computer program that has columns of data that are related. Each number in a spreadsheet has its own cell.

To represent a pattern, enter information for the first term. Use one or more operations to get the rest of the terms in the pattern.

For example, the spreadsheet below shows a pattern. The first term is $2.

	A	B
1	Term number	Cost
2	1	$2
3	2	$4
4	3	$8
5	4	$16

The formula to get the second term is B3 = 2*B2, the third term is B4 = 2*B3, and so on.

Solve a Simpler Problem

Goal Solve problems by using a simpler problem.

1. Use this pattern.

design 1   design 2   design 3

a) How many boxes are in design 8? Make a plan to solve the problem.

Suggested answer: I don't want to draw design 8, so I'll solve a simpler problem. I'll draw design 4. I'll make a table to compare the design number with the number of boxes.

I'll look for a pattern in the numbers in the table and see if the number of boxes for design 4 matches my drawing. Then I'll extend the table to design 8.

Carry out your plan.
Suggested answer:

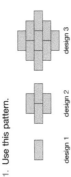

design 4

Design number	Number of boxes
1	1
2	4
3	9
4	16

I notice that if I multiply the design number by itself, I get the number of boxes.
1 × 1 = 1
2 × 2 = 4
3 × 3 = 9
4 × 4 = 16
For design 8, I predict that there will be 8 × 8 = 64 boxes.

b) How many boxes are in design 10?
Suggested answer:
10 × 10 = 100
100 boxes

At-Home Help

To solve some problems, it is easier to solve a simpler problem.

Make a Plan
Organize data using the simpler problem. If possible, use a table to arrange numbers and drawings.

Carry Out the Plan
Look for a pattern to relate the columns in your table.

Try to find an operation that works for all the rows in your table.

Write a pattern rule.

Check that your pattern rule works for the next simple problem. Draw a picture, if necessary, to check.

Use the pattern rule to solve the original problem.

Variables in Equations

Goal Solve equations including symbols representing variables.

> **At-Home Help**
>
> An equation can sometimes have more than one variable.
>
> For example, $A + O = 9$ and $A = O + O$ are equations with the variables A and O.
>
> To solve for A and O, use the expression $O + O$ for A in the first equation.
>
> $O + O + O = 9$
>
> Since three 3s are 9, O must be 3. Use 3 for O in the second equation to get $A = 3 + 3$. Since $3 + 3 = 6$, A must be 6.

1. A gym has twice as many soccer balls as basketballs. Altogether there are 36 balls.

   a) Explain what is represented by the equation $S + B = 36$.

   Suggested answer: It represents the total number of balls in the gym. S is the number of soccer balls. B is the number of basketballs. There are 36 balls.

   b) Explain what is represented by the equation $S = E + B$.

   Suggested answer: It represents the relationship between the number of soccer balls and the number of basketballs. The number of soccer balls is equal to two times the number of basketballs.

   c) How many basketballs are there? How many soccer balls are there?

   Suggested answer:
   $S + B = 36$ $S = B + B$, so I can replace S with $B + B$.
   $B + B + B = 36$
   $12 + 12 + 12 = 36$
   $B = 12$ and $S = 24$ There are 12 basketballs and 24 soccer balls.

2. In a granola recipe, there is three times as much oats as coconut. The total mass of oats and coconut is 600 g.

   a) Explain what is represented by the equation $O + C = 600$.

   Suggested answer: It represents the total mass. O represents the mass of oats. C represents the mass of coconut. The total mass is 600 g.

   b) Explain what is represented by the equation $O = C + C + C$.

   Suggested answer: It represents the relationship between the mass of oats and the mass of coconut. The mass of oats is equal to three times the mass of coconut.

   c) How many grams of each ingredient are there?

   Suggested answer:
   $O + C = 600$ I can replace O with $C + C + C$.
   $C + C + C + C = 600$
   I know $4 \times 150 = 600$, so there are 150 g of coconut and $O = C + C + C$ so there are 450 g of oats.

Equal Expressions

Goal Write equal expressions and determine the value of a missing term in an equation.

> **At-Home Help**
>
> An **expression** is a mathematical statement made with numbers or variables and operations.
>
> For example: $5 + 3 - 7$ is an expression with numbers only.
>
> $6 \times t$ is an expression with a variable.
>
> An **equation** is a mathematical statement that has an expression on each side of the equal sign. Both expressions must be equal in an equation.

1. Which expressions are equal? Use an equals sign. If they are not equal, change one expression to make them equal.

   a) $2 + 3 \;\boxed{=}\; 5 + 0$

   b) $1 + 7 \;\boxed{}\; 2 + 5$

   Suggested answer: $0 + 7 = 2 + 5$

   c) $8 + 6 \;\boxed{}\; 2 + 9$

   Suggested answer: $8 + 6 = 5 + 9$

   d) $3 + 8 \;\boxed{=}\; 6 + 5$

2. Replace each $\square$ so the expressions are equal.

   a) $5 + \square = 7 + 6$
   $\square = 8$

   b) $9 - 4 = \square + 3$
   $\square = 2$

   c) $\square \times 3 = 2 + 7$
   $\square = 3$

   d) $12 \div \square = 4 \times 3$
   $\square = 1$

3. Isabelle has five swim practices and three soccer practices this month. Judy has the same number of practices this month. Judy has two swim practices.

   a) Write an expression for the number of practices Isabelle has.
   $5 + 3$

   b) Write an expression for the number of practices Judy has.
   $2 + p$

   c) Write an equation with your expressions.
   $5 + 3 = 2 + p$

   d) How many soccer practices does Judy have? Explain what you did.

   Suggested answer: I know that $5 + 3 = 8$. So $2 + p = 8$. This means p is 6. Judy has 6 soccer practices. An expression for the number of practices Judy has is $2 + 6$. $5 + 3 = 2 + 6$ Both expressions have the same value.

Test Yourself   Page 1

Circle the correct answer.

1. One movie ticket costs $5.50. Which table shows the correct pattern?

A.

Number of tickets	Cost
1	$5.50
2	$10.00
3	$15.50
4	$20.00

B.

Number of tickets	Cost
1	$5.50
2	$11.00
3	$16.50
4	$22.00

C.

Number of tickets	Cost
1	$5.50
2	$6.50
3	$7.50
4	$8.50

D.

Number of tickets	Cost
1	$0
2	$5.50
3	$11.50
4	$16.50

2. Which pattern rule best represents the pattern in Question 1?

A. Add $5.50 to the term number.

B. Multiply $5.50 by 2.

C. Multiply $5.50 by the term number.

D. Add 1 to $5.50.

3. What is the cost of six movie tickets in Question 1?

A. $27.50

B. $30.00

C. $33.00

D. $33.50

4. Which pattern rule shows the total number of candies in any number of packages?

Number of packages	Total number of candies
1	3
2	6
3	9
4	12
5	15

A. $2 \times n$

B. $3 \times n$

C. $2 + n$

D. $3 + n$

5. What is the common difference in the pattern 18, 21, 24, 27, …?

A. 2

B. 3

C. 4

D. 5

Test Yourself   Page 2

6. What is the first term and the common difference in the pattern $1.50, $3.00, $4.50, $6.00, …?

A. $1.50, $1.50

B. $1.50, $3.00

C. $3.00, $1.50

D. $1.50, $2.00

7. What is the 10th term in the pattern in Question 6?

A. $12.00

B. $13.00

C. $14.00

D. $15.00

8. Which expressions are *not* equal?

A. $2 + 8$ and $6 + 4$

B. $9 - 5$ and 2×2

C. 3×4 and $8 + 2$

D. $7 + 1$ and $10 - 2$

9. Tilo has two red baseball caps and five green baseball caps. Michael has the same total number of baseball caps as Tilo. Michael has three green baseball caps. Which equation would you use to solve this problem?

A. $3 + 5 = 2 + c$

B. $2 + 3 = 5 + c$

C. $2 + c = 5 + 3$

D. $2 + 5 = c + 3$

10. How many red baseball caps does Michael have in Question 9?

A. 2

B. 3

C. 4

D. 5

11. A closet has three times as many hats as sweaters. The total number of hats and sweaters is 12. How many of each item is there?

A. 8 hats, 4 sweaters

B. 9 hats, 3 sweaters

C. 7 hats, 5 sweaters

D. 6 hats, 6 sweaters

Exploring Greater Numbers

 Goal Compare numbers to one million.

A bumblebee can flap its wings about 200 times per second.

A dragonfly can flap its wings about 38 times per second.

1. Predict how many times a dragonfly flaps its wings in 1000 s.

   Suggested answer:
   about 40 000 times
   I rounded 38 to 40 to estimate.
   40 × 1000 = 40 000

2. About how many hours would it take for a dragonfly to flap its wings 1 000 000 times? Show your work.

   Suggested answer:
   A dragonfly would have to flap its wings for about 25 000 s.
   1 000 000 ÷ 40 = 25 000
   60 s × 60 min = 3600 s in an hour
   I'll round 3600 s to 4000 s to estimate.
   25 000 ÷ 4000 = about 6
   A dragonfly would take about 6 h to flap it's wings 1 000 000 times.

3. a) About how many times can a bumblebee flap its wings in 1000 min?

   Suggested answer:
   In 1 min the bee flaps its wings about 200 × 60 = 12 000 times.
   So, in 1000 min the bee flaps its wings about 12 000 000 times.

   b) How many 1000 thousands is your answer in part a)?
   twelve 1000 thousands

Reading and Writing Numbers

 **Goal** Read, write, and describe numbers greater than 100 000.

1. Write each number in standard and expanded form.

   a)

   204 010
   200 000 + 4000 + 10

   b)

   1 329 027
   1 000 000 + 300 000 + 20 000 + 9000 + 20 + 7

2. Write each number as a numeral in standard form.

   a) four hundred forty thousand twenty-six
   440 026

   b) twenty-two thousand eight
   22 008

   c) seven hundred thirty-one thousand three hundred five
   731 305

3. Write the words for each number.

   a) 304 000 three hundred four thousand

   b) 21 000 twenty-one thousand

   c) 12 600 twelve thousand six hundred

4. The sun in our solar system takes about 240 million years to orbit once around the centre of the Milky Way galaxy. Write that number of years in standard form.
   240 000 000

Comparing and Ordering Numbers

 Goal Compare and order numbers to 1 000 000.

1. Compare each pair of numbers. Use an inequality sign.
   a) 602 589 < 640 077
   b) 314 806 < 409 116
   c) 584 192 < 521 009

2. Order the numbers in Question 1 from least to greatest.
   314 806, 409 116, 521 009, 584 192, 602 589, 640 077

3. List three numbers between 216 534 and 242 189.
   Suggested answer:
   218 965, 234 567, 240 139

4. a) The number 5□8 206 is between □96 872 and 512 093. The two missing digits are different. What might they be?
   Suggested answer:
   0 for 508 206
   4 for 496 872

   b) Order the numbers from part a) from least to greatest.
   496 872, 508 206, 512 093

Renaming Numbers

 Goal Rename numbers using place value concepts.

1. Complete each statement.
   a) 4 625 239 is about __5__ millions.
   b) 276 081 is about __0.3__ millions.
   c) 3 910 245 is about __4000__ thousands.

2. Irene takes pictures with her digital camera. The file sizes of four of her pictures are:
   3.2 MB 720 kB 21 500 bytes 408 350 bytes
   a) Write the first two file sizes as a number of bytes:
   3 200 000 bytes, 720 000 bytes
   b) Estimate each file size, except for the first one, as millions of bytes or megabytes.
   0.7 MB, 0.02 MB, 0.4 MB
   c) Which photo uses the most bytes?
   3.2 MB

3. Write each number in another form.
   a) 1.9 million = __1 900 000__ ones
   b) 4.6 million = __4600__ thousands
   c) 0.28 million = __2800__ hundreds

Communicate About Solving Problems

Goal Explain your thinking when solving a problem.

A city produced 183 million kilograms of landfill waste in 2016. In 2017, a composting program reduced the landfill waste to 45 million kilograms. About how much less waste was taken to the landfill each day in 2017? Explain how you solved the problem.

Suggested answer:
I write both values on a place value chart.

Millions			Thousands			Ones		
Hundreds	Tens	Ones	Hundreds	Tens	Ones	Hundreds	Tens	Ones
	●●●●●●●●●	●						
●	●●●●							

The difference is 138 million.
There are 365 days in a year. I divide 138 million by 365 to calculate how much less waste is taken to the landfill each day.

The problem asks "about how much" so my answer can be an estimate. I use rounded numbers that are easy to calculate with.
160 000 000 ÷ 400 = 400 000

About 400 000 kg less waste was taken to the landfill each day in 2017.

Reading and Writing Decimal Thousandths

Goal Read, write, and model decimals.

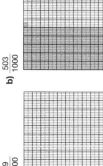
1. Write each fraction as a decimal.

   a) $\dfrac{29}{1000}$ 0.029

   b) $\dfrac{503}{1000}$ 0.503

   c) $\dfrac{790}{1000}$ 0.790

2. Colour a 1000ths grid to represent each fraction.

   a) $\dfrac{29}{1000}$ b) $\dfrac{503}{1000}$

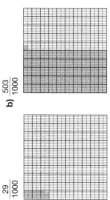

3. Write a decimal for each number.

   a) fifty-two hundreths _____ 0.52

   b) fifty-two thousandths _____ 0.052

4. Write a decimal to fit each description.

   a) one-tenth less than 6.302
      6.202

   b) one-thousandth greater than 6.302
      6.303

   c) one-hundredth greater than 6.302
      6.312

5. Write each answer in Question 3 in expanded form.

   a) 6 ones + 2 tenths + 2 thousandths   b) 6 ones + 3 tenths + 3 thousandths   c) 6 ones + 3 tenths + 1 hundredth + 2 thousandths

6. List two fractions that are equivalent to 0.400.
   Suggested answer: $\dfrac{4}{10}$ and $\dfrac{400}{1000}$

Rounding Decimals

 Goal Interpret rounded decimals and round decimals to the nearest tenth or hundredth.

At-Home Help

Decimal numbers can be rounded to the nearest tenth or hundredth.

For example, 0.286 rounds up to 0.29 (decimal hundredth) and 0.3 (decimal tenth).

A number line helps with rounding.

```
        0.286
         ↓
|++++++++|+++++++|+++++++|
0.280   0.290   0.300
```

1. Round each decimal to the nearest hundredth.

   a) 0.526
   0.53

   c) 0.078
   0.08

   b) 0.896
   0.90

   d) 3.006
   3.01

2. Round each decimal to the nearest tenth.

   a) 0.72
   0.7

   c) 2.462
   2.5

   b) 1.073
   1.1

   d) 0.98
   1.0

3. Which numbers below round to the same hundredth?
   2.417   2.423   2.024   2.400
   Suggested answer: 2.417 and 2.423 both round to 2.42.

4. Name a decimal thousandth that could be rounded as described below.

   a) up to 0.35 or down to 0.3
   Suggested answer: 0.348

   b) down to 2.12 or down to 2.1
   Suggested answer: 2.123

5. Maya cut strips of fabric to make a quilted design. Each piece measured 0.365 m. If she had measured to the nearest centimetre instead, what might the length of fabric be?
   0.37 m

Comparing and Ordering Decimals

 Goal Compare and order decimals to thousandths.

At-Home Help

To compare and order decimal numbers to thousandths, compare the digits in this order:
- ones
- tenths
- hundredths
- thousandths

You can also compare and order decimals by their positions on a number line.

1. Which decimal is greater?

   a) 2.03 or 2.4
   2.4

   c) 0.526 or 1.004
   1.004

   b) 5.7 or 3.99
   5.7

   d) 0.403 or 0.067
   0.403

2. Order these decimal numbers from least to greatest.

   a) 2.108   0.053   0.872   1.096
   0.053, 0.872, 1.096, 2.108

   b) 2.085   2.008   3.004   2.805
   2.008, 2.085, 2.805, 3.004

3. Which measurement is greater?

   a) 0.087 kg or 0.800 kg
   0.800 kg

   b) 4.312 km or 3567 m
   4.312 km

   c) 450 g or 1.088 kg
   1.088 kg

4. List the numbers of the form ☐.☐☐ between 1.3 and 1.5 that are greater than 140 hundredths.
   Suggested answer: 140 hundredths is the same as 1.4.
   The numbers greater than 1.4 are 1.41, 1.42, 1.43, 1.44, 1.45, 1.46, 1.47, 1.48, and 1.49.

Test Yourself Page 1

Circle the correct answer.

1. Which statement is true?

  A. 1 million = 100 thousands
  B. 1 million = 100000 hundreds
  C. 1 million = 1000 ten thousands
  D. 1 million = 10 hundred thousands

2. Which is the expanded form for 2506084?

  A. 2000000 + 50000 + 6000 + 80 + 4
  B. 2 millions + 5 hundred thousands + 6 hundreds + 84 ones
  C. 2000000 + 500000 + 6000 + 80 + 4
  D. 2 millions + 56 hundreds + 84 ones

3. Which inequality is incorrect?

  A. 206354 < 216089
  B. 706821 > 799035
  C. 907645 < 980004
  D. 625138 < 739156

4. What is the correct order of the numbers below from least to greatest?
  871052,   86304,   280546,   901034,   807621

  A. 86304, 280546, 871052, 807621, 901034
  B. 86304, 280546, 807621, 871052, 901034
  C. 86304, 901034, 871052, 807621, 280546
  D. 280546, 871052, 807621, 901034, 86304

5. Which estimate is correct?

  A. 1.7 MB is about 2 million bytes.
  B. 0.4 kB is about 1 thousand bytes.
  C. 3230050 bytes is about 300 kB.
  D. 89400 bytes is about 1 MB.

6. Which description fits for the number 876400?

  A. eighty-seven thousand sixty-four
  B. eight hundred seven thousand sixty-four
  C. eight hundred seven thousand six hundred forty
  D. eighty-seven thousand six hundred forty

Test Yourself Page 2

7. Which math statement is incorrect?

  A. $\frac{52}{1000} = 0.052$
  B. $\frac{206}{1000} = 0.206$
  C. $\frac{79}{1000} = 0.790$
  D. $\frac{358}{1000} = 0.358$

8. Which decimal represents the fraction $\frac{28}{1000}$?

  A. 0.028
  B. 0.280
  C. 0.208
  D. 2.800

9. Which fraction represents the decimal 0.403?

  A. $\frac{43}{100}$
  B. $\frac{43}{1000}$
  C. $\frac{403}{1000}$
  D. $\frac{430}{1000}$

10. Which numbers below round to the same hundredth?
  4.806   3.987   4.813   4.811

  A. 3.987, 4.806, 4.813
  B. 3.987, 4.811, 4.813
  C. 4.806, 4.811, 4.813
  D. 3.987, 4.806, 4.811

11. Which number would be 2.065 rounded to the nearest tenth?

  A. 2.0
  B. 2.1
  C. 2.5
  D. 2.6

12. What is the order of the numbers below from least to greatest?
  1.804,   2.053,   1.692,   0.982,   1.086

  A. 0.982, 1.804, 1.086, 1.692, 2.053
  B. 0.982, 1.086, 1.804, 1.692, 2.053
  C. 0.982, 1.086, 1.692, 1.804, 2.053
  D. 0.982, 1.692, 1.804, 1.086, 2.053

Creating and Analyzing a Survey

 Goal Collect, organize, and display the results of a survey.

Trudy wants to know about TV-watching habits of students in her school. She wrote a question for a survey.

1. How often *do you watch TV?*
   a) never
   b) once or twice a week
   c) three times a week
   d) more than three times a week
   e) every day

1. What is another survey question Trudy could ask?
   Suggested answer:
   Question 2: *What time of day do you watch TV?*
   a) morning   b) midday   c) afternoon
   d) evening   e) late at night

2. Trudy asked the students in her school for how long they watch TV at any one time. She recorded the results in a tally chart.

About 1 h	About 2 h	About 3 h	About 4 h	More than 4 h
‖‖	‖‖ ‖‖‖	‖‖‖	‖‖	‖

Sketch a graph to display the results.

Suggested answer:

Length of Time Students Watch TV at a Time

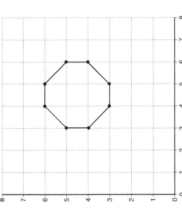

3. Explain why you chose the kind of graph you did.
   Suggested answer: I chose a circle graph because I wanted to show how the possible answers for the survey question compared to each other and to the whole. The circle represents the total number of students surveyed.

Plotting Coordinate Pairs

Goal Plot points on a grid and locate them using coordinate pairs.

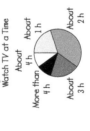
Yuri is plotting the shape of a stop sign he saw on a street.

1. Plot the points (3, 4), (3, 5), (4, 6), and (5, 6) on the grid. Connect the points in order.

2. Draw the rest of the sign on the grid above.

3. What coordinate pairs did you use to complete the sign?
   (6, 5), (6, 4), (5, 3), and (4, 3)

4. What shape is the sign?
   an octagon

Page 23

Line Graphs

Goal Create and interpret line graphs.

1. Sui earns money shovelling snow from his neighbour's sidewalk. He wants to know the length of sidewalk he must shovel to earn $5.00. He recorded the distance he shovelled and how much he earned.

Distance (m)	4	8	12	16
Earnings	$1.00	$2.00	$3.00	$4.00

a) Use the data in the table to create a graph.
Suggested answer:

Earnings Compared to Distance Shovelled

b) Describe how your graph appears.
Suggested answer: The graph is a straight line that shows earnings going up with distance.

c) Estimate how much Sui earns for a distance of 8.3 m.
about $2.10

d) Predict the distance Sui must shovel to earn $5.00. Explain your reasoning.
20 m
Suggested answer: Sui earns $2.00 when he shovels 8 m. He earns $3.00 when he shovels 12 m. So to earn $5.00, he must shovel 8 m + 12 m = 20 m.

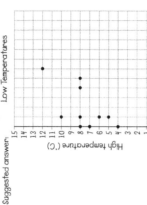

At-Home Help

A **line graph** is a graph of a line through points. This type of graph shows how the change in one value is related to a change in another value.

For example, the graph below is a line graph showing the distance a bicycle travels over time.

Distance Bicycle Travels Over Time

To predict how far the bicycle will travel in 20 s, you can either extend the graph or use estimation. It takes 4 s for the bicycle to travel 5 m. So in 20 s the bicycle will travel about 25 m.

Page 24

Scatter Plots

Goal Create and interpret scatter plots.

The table below shows the low and high daily temperatures in Victoria, British Columbia, for two weeks.

Day	Low temperature (°C)	High temperature (°C)	Day	Low temperature (°C)	High temperature (°C)
Dec. 19	6	12	Dec. 26	5	8
Dec. 20	1	10	Dec. 27	1	8
Dec. 21	1	10	Dec. 28	0	7
Dec. 22	0	8	Dec. 29	1	5
Dec. 23	0	7	Dec. 30	4	8
Dec. 24	4	8	Dec. 31	1	6
Dec. 25	5	8	Jan. 1	0	4

1. Compare the high and low temperatures. Use a scatter plot.
Suggested answer:

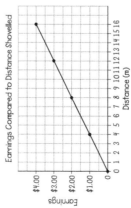

High Temperatures Compared to Low Temperatures

2. Describe how the points appear on the scatter plot. Identify the most common low and high temperatures.

Suggested answer: Most of the points are near the middle left of the scatter plot. The most common low temperature is 1°C because it appears five times in the data. The most common high temperature is 8°C because it appears six times in the data.

At-Home Help

A **scatter plot** is a graph made by plotting coordinate pairs to show if one set of data can be used to make predictions about another set of data.

For example, the goals and wins of several hockey teams are plotted on the scatter plot below.

Wins Compared to Goals

Each point on this scatter plot is determined using the goals for the first coordinate and the wins for the second coordinate. If a team scored 262 goals and had 43 wins, you would plot the point (262, 43) on the scatter plot.

Mean and Median

Goal Use mean and median to compare sets of data.

1. Determine the mean and median of each set of numbers.

   a) 8, 0, 2, 7, 1, 7, 3   mean: 4   median: 3

   b) 2, 3, 6, 0, 0, 1, 1   mean: 1.9   median: 1

   c) 7, 0, 9, 0   mean: 4   median: 3.5

   d) 18, 11, 22, 9, 5, 0   mean: 9.2   median: 10

2. Zoë recorded how long each of her friends walked on two days.

Student	Time on day 1 (min)	Time on day 2 (min)
Clara	20	25
Jose	10	9
Tia	15	18
Nicolas	8	20
Mario	18	19
Tim	5	17
Leah	12	8

   a) Determine the median time for each day.

   Day 1 mean: 12.7 min, median: 12 min
   Day 2 mean: 16.6 min, median: 18 min

   b) On which day did the most walking occur?

   day 2

3. Sara said that the median does not have to be one of the numbers in a set. Is her statement correct? Explain.

   Suggested answer: Yes. If the median is not in a set of numbers, it must be between the two numbers in the middle. The median cannot be less than the least value in a set. Also, the median cannot be greater than the greatest value in a set.

Changing the Intervals on a Graph

Goal Describe how changing the number of intervals changes a graph.

Jinji recorded how much his family spent at restaurants during the last year. He sketched a graph of his data.

Month	Amount
Jan.	$40
Feb.	$80
Mar.	$30
Apr.	$64
May	$31
Jun.	$35
Jul.	$45
Aug.	$46
Sept.	$28
Oct.	$48
Nov.	$30
Dec.	$60

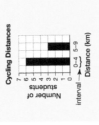

1. Graph Jinji's data. Use one-month intervals.

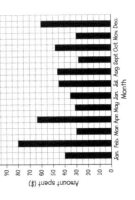

2. Describe the difference between Jinji's graph and your graph.

   Suggested answer:
   On my graph, three of the bars are about the same height.
   On my graph, you can see the amount spent each month.
   The amount spent each month cannot be determined from Jinji's graph.

Changing the Scale on a Graph

Goal Describe how changing the scale changes a line graph.

Charmaine wants to know how fast a bowl of hot soup cools. She measured the temperature of the soup every minute.

Time (min)	0	1	2	3	4	5	6	7	8	9	10
Temperature (°C)	70	68	65	62	58	55	53	51	49	46	45

1. Sketch a line graph of Charmaine's data.

Suggested answer:

Temperature of Soup Over Time

2. What scale did you use for the vertical axis?
Suggested answer: 0–70°C increasing by 10°C

What scale did you use for the horizontal axis?
Suggested answer: 0–10 min increasing by 1 min

3. Predict how your graph in Question 1 would change if you doubled the value of each unit on the scale of the vertical axis. Sketch the line graph to check your prediction.

Suggested answer:
The graph will not go down as suddenly as in Question 1.

Temperature of Soup Over Time

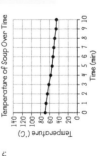

Communicate About Conclusions from Data Displays

Goal Use data presented in tables, charts, and graphs to create an argument.

1. A newspaper printed this scatter plot with the headline "Drinking More Water Means Fewer Colds."

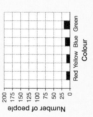

Volume of Water Consumed Compared to Number of Colds in a Year

Write a letter to the editor about the headline and the scatter plot. Use the Communication Checklist

Suggested answer:

Dear Editor: The points at the top left of the scatter plot show that the people who drank 1.5 L of water or more had fewer colds. The points at the bottom right show that the people who drank less than 1.5 L of water had more colds. The problem with these conclusions is that people who drank 2.0 L or 1.5 L of water had anywhere from 1 to 4 colds. Also, there are not enough data points so you can't draw accurate conclusions. There are many factors that affect a person getting a cold. You can't conclude that there is a clear relationship between volume of water drunk and number of colds from the scatter plot.

Test Yourself   Page 1

Circle the correct answer.

1. Mia surveyed 20 students to find out how many hours they surf the Internet each week.

Survey results					
2	5	4	3	10	5
8	1	3	4	6
7	5	2	3	6
9	3	4	6	7

Which tally chart best represents Mia's data?

A.

Hours	Number of students
0–2 h	////
3–4 h	++++
5–6 h	++++
7–8 h	///
9–10 h	////

B.

Hours	Number of students
0–5 h	++++ ++++ /
6–10 h	++++ ////

C.

Hours	Number of students
0–2 h	///
3–4 h	++++ /
5–6 h	++++ /
7–8 h	///
9–10 h	++++ ++++

D.

Hours	Number of students
0–5 h	++++ ++++
6–10 h	++++ ++++

2. Which coordinates describe the shape to the right?

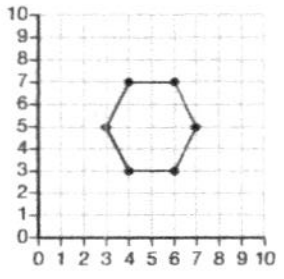

A. (3, 4), (5, 7), (3, 6), (5, 3), (7, 4), and (7, 6)

B. (4, 3), (7, 5), (6, 3), (3, 5), (4, 7), and (6, 7)

C. (4, 4), (6, 4), (7, 5), (3, 5), (4, 8), and (6, 8)

D. (4, 4), (4, 6), (5, 7), (5, 3), (8, 4), and (8, 6)

Denise filled a water pitcher with water and then emptied it. Use the line graph to answer Questions 3 and 4.

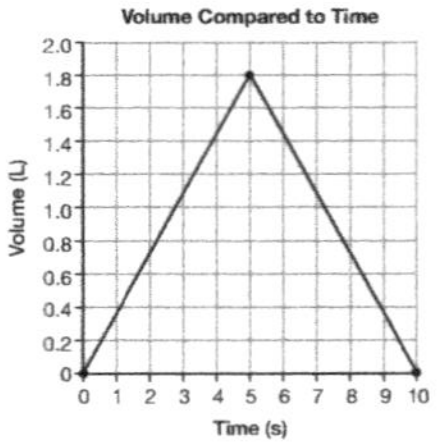

3. During which time interval is the pitcher being filled?

A. 0–4 s   **C.** 5–10 s

B. 0–5 s   **D.** 6–10 s

4. About how long did it take to fill the pitcher with 1 L of water?

A. about 1 s   **B.** about 2 s

C. about 3 s   **D.** about 4 s

Volume Compared to Time

Constructing Graphic Organizers

Goal   Use Venn diagrams and Carroll diagrams to describe relationships between two sets of data.

Monique wants to know if many countries have both yellow and red on their flags.

Country	Colours on flag
Nigeria	green, white
India	orange, white, red, blue
Philippines	yellow, red, white, blue
Belgium	black, yellow, red
Sweden	blue, yellow
Italy	green, white, red
Canada	red, white
Colombia	yellow, blue, red

At-Home Help

A **Venn diagram** is a drawing with circles inside a rectangle. This type of diagram is helpful when sorting items in a set.

For example, in the Venn diagram below, one circle represents "Dog" and the other circle represents "Cat." Students who have both a dog and a cat are listed where the circles overlap. Since Victor does not have a dog or a cat, his name is listed outside the circles but inside the rectangle.

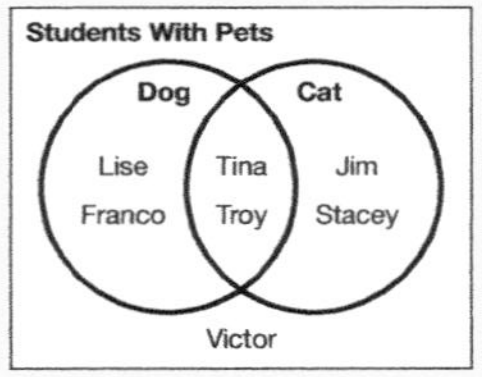

Students With Pets

A **Carroll diagram** is a chart that shows relationships using rows and columns.

For example, a Carroll diagram for the data shown in the Venn diagram above would be

	Boy	Girl
Dog	Franco, Troy	Lise, Tina
Cat	Jim, Troy	Stacey, Tina

1. **a)** Draw a Venn diagram to sort the countries by flag colour.

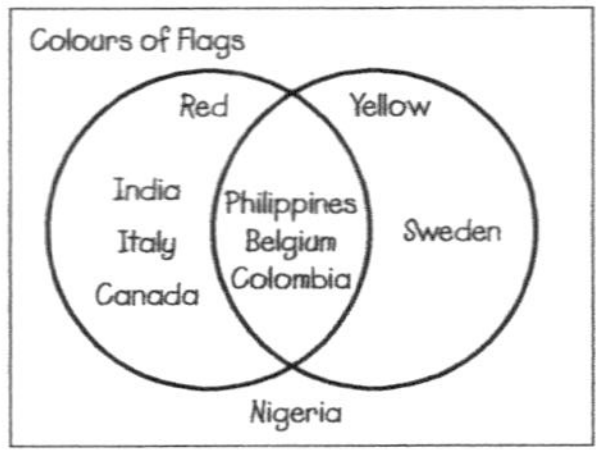

Colours of Flags

b) Which countries have both yellow and red on their flags?

Philippines, Belgium, and Colombia

c) Which country does not have yellow or red?

Nigeria

2. Use the data in the chart above to complete the Carroll diagram.

	1 or 2 colours	More than 2 colours
Red	Canada	India, Philippines, Belgium, Italy, Colombia
Yellow	Sweden	Philippines, Belgium, Colombia

Test Yourself   Page 2

5. What is the mean and median of this set of numbers?
   5, 13, 9, 15, 8

   A. 10 and 13   B. 5 and 9   C. 10 and 11   **D. 10 and 9**

6. Katrina timed the distance she cycled each day.

   What would the graph look like if she decreased the value of each unit on the vertical scale?

   A. The graph would look more flat.
   B. The graph would go down more suddenly.
   C. The graph would go up more suddenly.
   D. The graph would look the same.

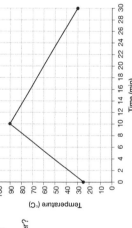

Cycling Distance Compared to Time

7. Clive made a Carroll diagram to sort the numbers from 1 to 20.
   What labels are missing in each column?

	?	?
Less than or equal to 10	4, 8	1, 2, 3, 5, 6, 7, 9, 10
Greater than 10	12, 16, 20	11, 13, 14, 15, 17, 18, 19

   A. Even numbers, Odd numbers
   B. Multiples of 2, Not multiples of 2
   C. Multiples of 3, Not multiples of 3
   D. Multiples of 4, Not multiples of 4

8. Teresa boiled some water for tea, then poured the tea and let it cool down. When did Teresa stop heating the water?

   A. from 0 min to 10 min
   B. at 10 min
   C. from 10 min to 30 min
   D. from 0 min to 30 min

Temperature of Tea Over Time

Adding and Subtracting Whole Numbers

Goal   Use mental math strategies to calculate sums and differences.

At-Home Help

Rounding is a mental math strategy for adding and subtracting numbers. When you round, you will need to adjust your answer to get the exact answer.

For example:
23 + 58 can be rounded to
20 + 60 = 80. 23 is 3 more than 20 and 58 is 2 less than 60. So adjust your answer by adding 1.
The answer is 81.
76 − 40 can be rounded to
80 − 40 = 40. 76 is 4 less than 80.
So adjust your answer by subtracting 4. The answer is 36.

Regrouping is another mental math strategy for adding and subtracting numbers. Regroup numbers into 5s or 10s to make calculations easier.

For example:
43 + 92 can be regrouped as
(43 + 2) + 90.
The answer is 45 + 90 = 135.
80 − 19 can be regrouped as
(80 − 10) − 9.
The answer is 70 − 9 = 61.

1. Use mental math to calculate each sum. Describe your strategy.

   a) 680 + 210 = __890__

   Regroup 600 + 200 + (80 + 10) = 600 + 200 + 90, or 890.

   b) 763 + 847 + 289 = __1899__

   Round 289 to nearest hundred, then regroup to get
   750 + (847 + 3) + (300 + 10) = 750 + 850 + 310, or 1910.
   289 is 11 less than 300. So subtract 11 from 1910.

2. Use mental math to calculate each sum.

   a) 545 + 655 = __1200__   d) 715 + 903 + 422 = __2040__
   b) 874 + 926 = __1800__   e) 1822 + 428 + 650 = __2900__
   c) 766 + 704 = __1470__   f) 2016 + 624 + 910 = __3550__

3. Use mental math to calculate each difference. Describe your strategy.

   a) 680 − 490 = __190__

   If the question was 690 − 490, the answer would be 200. 680 is 10 less than 690. So subtract 10 from 200.

   b) 1650 − 95 = __1555__

   Round 95 to nearest hundred to get 1650 − 100 = 1550. 95 is 5 less than 100. So add 5 to 1550.

4. Use mental math to calculate each difference.

   a) 820 − 450 = __370__   c) 903 − 237 = __520__
   b) 625 − 175 = __450__   d) 1020 − 500 = __666__
   e) 3005 − 755 = __2250__
   f) 2103 − 487 = __1616__

Estimating Sums and Differences

 Goal Estimate sums and differences to solve problems.

At-Home Help

To solve problems, use estimation if the problem does not ask for an exact answer.

Round to the place value that gives you numbers that are easy to add or subtract. You might adjust your rounding up or down, depending on the numbers.

Sometimes you may want to use more than one strategy to solve the problem.

Always check if your answer is reasonable.

Remember to show all your work.

1. Which sums are greater than 2200?
   a) 840 + 622 + 713   less than 2200
   b) 372 + 923 + 987   greater than 2200
   c) 565 + 834 + 879   greater than 2200
   d) 703 + 543 + 824   less than 2200

2. Which differences are less than 540?
   a) 1280 − 640   greater than 540
   b) 6080 − 5590   less than 540
   c) 4608 − 3024   greater than 540
   d) 8146 − 7870   less than 540

3. A mountain-climbing contest had teams climb two different mountains. One team climbed Mount Everest. It has a height of 8848 m. Another team climbed Mount Logan in the Yukon Territory. It has a height of 5959 m. About how much higher did the Mount Everest team climb? Describe your strategy.

   About 2800 m. Round 8848 and 5959 to nearest hundred to get 8800 − 6000 = 2800.

4. Sam recorded the forms of transportation used by neighbourhood students to get to school. The neighbourhood will win an award if more than 5000 students use a physically active form of transportation to get to school.

Form of transportation	Number of students
walk	3162
bicycle	1072
bus	2154
car	936
other (skateboard, inline skates, etc.)	636

   Will Sam's neighbourhood win the award? Describe your strategy.

   No. Round numbers to nearest thousand or hundred to get 3000 + 1000 + 600 = 4600.
   About 4600 students use a physically active form of transportation.

Adding Whole Numbers

 Goal Solve problems by adding four 3-digit whole numbers.

At-Home Help

To add numbers, add digits with the same place value.

Check your answer using estimation.

For example:
```
  1 1
  2 1 3          2 1 3
  3 2 7      or  3 2 7
  1 6 3          1 6 3
+ 2 0 4        + 2 0 4
  9 0 7          8 0 0
                  9 0
                  1 7
                9 0 7
```

Estimate:
200 + 300 + 200 + 200 = 900

1. Calculate.
```
a)  1 2        b)  3 2 9       c)  1 1
    2 0 6          4 6 2           4 2 1
    3 4 9          5 0 3           2 3 0
    1 2 7        + 3 6 8           3 2 9
  + 4 6 7          1 5 0 0       + 5 4 7
    1 1 4 9         1 4 0         1 5 2 7
                      2 2
                    1 6 6 2
```

2. During summer camp, Cecilia's group planted trees on five days. The group planted 154 trees on the first day, 183 trees on the second day, 189 trees on the third day, and 196 trees on the fifth day. The group planted a total of 934 trees.

   a) How many trees were planted on the fourth day? Show your work.
   212 trees
```
    3 2          9 3 4
    1 5 4      − 7 2 2
    1 8 3        2 1 2
    1 8 9
  + 1 9 6
    7 2 2
```

   b) Use estimation to check if your answer is reasonable.
   Round 154 down and the other numbers up.
   100 + 200 + 200 + 200 = 700   900 − 700 = 200
   My estimate of 200 is close to 212. So my answer is reasonable.

3. Balvinder sells chocolate bars to raise money for his school. From Monday to Friday, Balvinder sold $676 worth of chocolate bars. On Monday he sold $117, on Tuesday he sold $130, on Wednesday he sold $143, and on Friday he sold $156. Calculate how much he sold on Thursday. Show your work.

   $130
```
    $117        $676
    $130      − $546
    $143        $130
  + $156
    $156
                4 0 0
                1 3 0
                 1 6
              $5 4 6
```

Subtracting Whole Numbers

Goal Subtract whole numbers to solve problems.

1. Estimate and then subtract. Show your work.

a) 8702 − 6914
Estimate: more or less than 2000?

less

$$\begin{array}{r} 16 \quad 9 \\ 7 \; \cancel{8} \; \cancel{10} 12 \\ \cancel{8} \cancel{7} \cancel{0} \cancel{2} \\ -6 \; 9 \; 1 \; 4 \\ \hline 1 \; 7 \; 8 \; 8 \end{array}$$

c) 64 902 − 5964
Estimate: more or less than 60 000?

less

$$\begin{array}{r} 13 \; 18 \quad 9 \\ 5 \; \cancel{8} \; \cancel{8} \; \cancel{10} 12 \\ 6 \cancel{4} \cancel{9} \cancel{0} \cancel{2} \\ -\;\; 5 \; 9 \; 6 \; 4 \\ \hline 5 \; 8 \; 9 \; 3 \; 8 \end{array}$$

b) 10 550 − 9845
Estimate: more or less than 1000?

less

Add 155 to both numbers.
10 550 + 155 = 10 705
9845 + 155 = 10 000

$$\begin{array}{r} 1 \; 0 \; 7 \; 0 \; 5 \\ -1 \; 0 \; 0 \; 0 \; 0 \\ \hline 7 \; 0 \; 5 \end{array}$$

d) 56 003 − 7894
Estimate: more or less than 46 000?

more

$$\begin{array}{r} 15 \quad 9 \quad 9 \\ 4 \; \cancel{8} \; \cancel{10} \; \cancel{10} 13 \\ 5 \cancel{6} \cancel{0} \cancel{0} \cancel{3} \\ -\;\; 7 \; 8 \; 9 \; 4 \\ \hline 4 \; 8 \; 1 \; 0 \; 9 \end{array}$$

2. Rico's home town had a population of 75 692 people in 1990. In 2000, the population was 83 020 people. By how much did the population increase? Determine if your answer is reasonable using estimation. Show your work.

7328 people
Add 8 to both numbers.   83 020 + 8 = 83 028
75 692 + 8 = 75 700

$$\begin{array}{r} 8 \; 3 \; 0 \; 2 \; 8 \\ -7 \; 5 \; 7 \; 0 \; 0 \\ \hline 7 \; 3 \; 2 \; 8 \end{array}$$

Estimate: 85 000 − 75 000 = 10 000
My estimate of 10 000 is close to 7328. So my answer is reasonable.

At–Home Help

To subtract numbers, start subtracting from the smallest place value. Regroup if you need to.

For example:

$$\begin{array}{r} 10 \\ 7 \; \cancel{8} \; 12 \\ 5 \; \cancel{8} \; \cancel{7} \; 2 \\ -2 \; 6 \; 4 \; 9 \\ \hline 3 \; 1 \; 6 \; 3 \end{array}$$

You can also add a number to both numbers to get numbers that are easier to subtract.

For example, add 51 to both numbers.   5812 + 51 = 5863
2649 + 51 = 2700

$$\begin{array}{r} 5 \; 8 \; 6 \; 3 \\ -2 \; 7 \; 0 \; 0 \\ \hline 3 \; 1 \; 6 \; 3 \end{array}$$

Check your answer using estimation or addition.

Estimate: 5800 − 2600 = 3200

Adding and Subtracting Decimal Numbers

Goal Use mental math strategies to calculate sums and differences.

Samantha, Matthew, and Akira went to buy some clothes from a charity fundraiser.

$9.95 $7.90 $0.80 $2.80 $8.75

1. **a)** Samantha has $22.00. Choose three items she can buy.

   Suggested answer: 1 jacket, 1 hat, and 1 sweater

   b) Use mental math to calculate the total cost. What bills and coins can she use to pay for the items?

   (using answer above) $21.50   one $20 bill, one loonie, and two quarters

   c) Use mental math to calculate Samantha's change.

   _$0.50_

2. Akira has $18.75 and Matthew has $24.50. How much more money does Matthew have than Akira? Use mental math to calculate your answer.

   _$5.75_

3. **a)** Choose three items that Akira can buy. Use mental math to calculate the total cost.

   Suggested answer: 1 pair of gloves, 1 sweater, and 1 shirt (total cost) $17.45

   b) Use mental math to calculate Akira's change.

   _$1.30_

At–Home Help

To add or subtract money amounts mentally, regroup the numbers to make the calculations easier.

Remember to check if your answers are reasonable.

For example, to add
$6.95 + $3.25 + $7.75, regroup.

7.00 − 0.05 + 3.00 + 0.25 + 7.00
+ 0.75 = 7.00 + 3.00 + 7.00 − 0.05
+ 0.25 + 0.75
= 17.00 − 0.05 + 1.00
= 18.00 − 0.05
= $17.95

Adding Decimals

Goal Add decimals using base ten blocks and pencil and paper.

1. Estimate and then add. Show your work.

a) 0.56 + 0.98
Estimate: 0.5 + 1 = 1.5
```
    1
  0.5 6
+ 0.9 8
-------
  1.4 0
  0.1 4
-------
  1.5 4
```

b) 2.804 + 0.426
Estimate: 3 + 0.5 = 3.5
```
  1   1
  2.8 0 4
+ 0.4 2 6
---------
  3.2 3 0
```

c) 0.897 + 5.824
Estimate: 1 + 6 = 7
```
  0.8 9 7
+ 5.8 2 4
---------
  5.0 0 0
  1.6 0 0
  0.1 1 0
  0.0 1 1
---------
  6.7 2 1
```

d) 3.498 + 2.635 + 0.384
Estimate: 3 + 3 + 0.3 = 6.3
```
  1 2 1
  3.4 9 8
  2.6 3 5
+ 0.3 8 4
---------
  6.5 1 7
```

e) 4.675 + 3.899 + 0.269
Estimate: 5 + 4 = 9
```
  4.6 7 5
  3.8 9 9
+ 0.2 6 9
---------
  7.0 0 0
  1.6 0 0
  0.2 2 0
  0.0 2 3
---------
  8.8 4 3
```

f) 4.8 + 3.152 + 0.59
Estimate: 5 + 3 + 1 = 9
```
  1 1
  4.8 0 0
  3.1 5 2
+ 0.5 9 0
---------
  8.5 4 2
```

At-Home Help

Decimal tenths, hundredths, and thousandths are added using the same rules as whole numbers.
- It is easier to add vertically if the decimal points are aligned.
- Add place values that are the same.
- If the sum of a place value is 10 or more, regroup using the next greater place value.
- Check your answer using estimation.

For example:
```
  2 1 1
  0.7 6 2
  0.4 5
  0.8 0 3
+ 0.1 0 7
---------
  2.1 2 2
```

Estimate:
0.8 + 0.4 + 0.8 + 0.1 = 2.1

To add a decimal number that has only tenth and hundredth place values and a decimal number that has a thousandth place value, add a zero for the thousandth place value.

For example, calculating 1.34 + 0.379 is the same as 1.340 + 0.379. Answer is 1.719.

Subtracting Decimals

Goal Subtract decimals using base ten blocks and pencil and paper.

1. Estimate and then subtract. Show your work.

a) 5.0 − 2.3
Estimate: 5 − 2 = 3
```
    4 10
  5̶.0̶
− 2.3
-----
  2.7
```

b) 8.21 − 3.63
Estimate: 8 − 3 = 5
Add 0.37 to both numbers.
8.21 + 0.37 = 8.58
3.63 + 0.37 = 4.00
```
  8.5 8
− 4.0 0
-------
  4.5 8
```

c) 4.020 − 1.989
Estimate: 4 − 2 = 2
```
    9 11
  3 10 X 10
  4̶.0̶2̶0̶
− 1.9 8 9
---------
  2.0 3 1
```

d) 6.411 − 2.58
Estimate: 6.5 − 2.5 = 4
Add 0.42 to both numbers.
6.411 + 0.42 = 6.831
2.58 + 0.42 = 3.00
```
  6.8 3 1
− 3.0 0 0
---------
  3.8 3 1
```

e) 9.05 − 6.208
Estimate: 9 − 6 = 3
```
    8 10 4 10
  9̶.0̶5̶0̶
− 6.2 0 8
---------
  2.8 4 2
```

f) 3.8 − 0.058
Estimate: 4 − 0 = 4
Add 0.942 to both numbers.
3.8 + 0.942 = 4.742
0.058 + 0.942 = 1.000
```
  4.7 4 2
− 1.0 0 0
---------
  3.7 4 2
```

At-Home Help

Decimal tenths, hundredths, and thousandths are subtracted using the same rules as whole numbers.
- It is easier to subtract vertically if the decimal points are aligned.
- Subtract place values that are the same, starting from the smallest place value.
- If you can't find the difference for a particular place value, regroup using the next greater place value.
- Check your answer using estimation or addition.

For example:
```
      9 9
  2 10 10 10
  3̶.0̶0̶0̶
− 0.7 5 7
---------
  2.2 4 3
```

You can also add a number to both numbers to get numbers that are easier to subtract.

For example, add 0.243 to both numbers.

3.000 + 0.243 = 3.243
0.757 + 0.243 = 1.000
```
  3.2 4 3
− 1.0 0 0
---------
  2.2 4 3
```

To subtract a decimal number that has only tenth and hundredth place values from a decimal number that has a thousandth place value, add a zero for the thousandth place value.
For example, calculating 3.25 − 1.722 is the same as 3.250 − 1.722.

Communicate About Solving a Multi-Step Problem

Goal Explain a solution to a problem.

Twyla wants to add 1 kg of compost to two vegetable gardens. One garden measures 6.00 m by 3.60 m. The other garden measures 7.60 m by 5.30 m. One kilogram of compost is needed for 43 m². Does Twyla have enough compost for both gardens? Write a solution. Determine if your answer is reasonable. Use the Communication Checklist.

Suggested answer:

Understand the Problem

I need to determine if Twyla has enough compost for both gardens. Make a Plan: This problem will take more than one step and more than one operation to solve. First I need to multiply to find the area of each garden. Then I need to add to find the total area. I can compare the total area with the area that 1 kg will cover, or 43 m².

Carry Out the Plan:

Area of one garden: 6.00 m × 3.60 m = 21.60 m²
Area of other garden: 7.60 m × 5.30 m = 40.28 m²

$$\begin{array}{r} 21.60 \text{ m}^2 \\ + 40.28 \text{ m}^2 \\ \hline 61.88 \text{ m}^2 \end{array}$$

Total area: 61.88 m² > 43 m²
So Twyla does not have enough compost for both gardens.

Look Back: Check whether calculations are reasonable. Round all numbers in the problem to the nearest whole number:
Area of one garden: 6 m × 4 m = 24 m²
Area of other garden: 8 m × 5 m = 40 m²
Total estimated area: 24 m² + 40 m² > 43 m²
My estimated answer for the problem shows that Twyla does not have enough compost for both gardens. So my calculated answer is reasonable.

At-Home Help

To solve problems, follow these steps.

Understand the Problem
• What are you asked to find out?
• What information is given?
• What information is necessary to solve the problem?

Make a Plan
• Is there more than one step needed to solve the problem?
• What calculations can be used?

Carry Out the Plan
• Show all your work.

Look Back
• Check whether your answer is reasonable.
Use the Communication Checklist.

Communication Checklist
☑ Did you explain your thinking?
☑ Did you show how you calculated each step?
☑ Did you explain how you checked each answer?
☑ Did you show the right amount of detail?

Test Yourself Page 1

Circle the correct answer.

1. Using estimation, which question has an answer greater than 1600?

   A. 569 + 872 + 236 ⟵circled   **C.** 379 + 406 + 765

   B. 264 + 504 + 429   **D.** 596 + 604 + 366

Use the survey results to answer Questions 2 and 3.

Favourite food	Number of students
chili	214
pizza	307
curried chicken	234
sushi	209

2. About how many students were surveyed?

   A. about 850   **B.** about 980   **C.** about 800   **D.** about 950 ⟵circled

3. How many more students chose pizza than sushi?

   A. 86 students   **B.** 89 students   **C.** 98 students ⟵circled   **D.** 96 students

4. Which calculation is *not* reasonable?

   A. 604 + 392 + 850 + 723 = 2569

   B. 824 − 368 = 456

   C. 356 + 147 + 520 + 801 = 1824 ⟵circled

   D. 18 011 − 9234 = 7777 ⟵circled

5. What are the missing numbers from top to bottom?

$$\begin{array}{r} 6\ 2\ 5\ 2\ \square \\ -\ \square\ 7\ \square\ 3 \\ \hline \square\ 3\ \square\ 2\ 8 \end{array}$$

   A. 1, 8, 9, 5, 6   **B.** 1, 8, 9, 5, 7 ⟵circled   **C.** 1, 8, 0, 5, 8   **D.** 1, 9, 9, 5, 7

Use the chart to answer Questions 6 and 7.

Juice	Volume (L)
orange	2.615
apple	2.365
cranberry	2.130
mango	3.090

6. What is the total volume of juice?

   A. 10.300 L   **B.** 10.200 L ⟵circled   **C.** 10.090 L   **D.** 9.090 L

7. How much more mango juice is there than orange juice?

   A. 1.475 L   **B.** 1.685 L   **C.** 0.685 L   **D.** 0.475 L ⟵circled

Measuring Length

Goal Select an appropriate measuring unit.

1. State an appropriate unit for each length.

   a) the distance you travel to go to school
      kilometres

   b) the thickness of a coin
      millimetres

   c) the height of a house
      metres

   d) the width of a book
      centimetres

2. Explain why you chose the unit you did for one answer in Question 1.
   Suggested answer: I chose centimetres for the width of a book because metres are too large to use and millimetres are too small to use.

3. Give an example of an item that might be measured in these units.

   a) metres
      Suggested answer: length of fabric

   b) millimetres
      Suggested answer: thickness of a card

   c) centimetres
      Suggested answer: length of a book

   d) kilometres
      Suggested answer: height of a tall mountain

Test Yourself   Page 2

Use the picture below to answer Questions 8 and 9.

$3.35 $1.75 $1.95 $0.75 $2.95

8. What is the total cost of the items shown?

   A. $10.65   B. $7.45   C. $10.50   D. $11.05

9. Kittie bought a can of nuts, a package of dried fruit, and a muffin with a $10 bill.
   How much change should she receive?

   A. $1.75   B. $0.85   **C. $1.85**   D. $0.75

10. Jasmine is making a fruit cake. The recipe has a combination of fruits and nuts.
    What is the total mass of fruit and nuts in the fruit cake?

Ingredient	Mass (kg)
currants	0.450
raisins	0.525
almonds	0.175
candied peel	0.175

    A. 1.200 kg   **B. 1.325 kg**   C. 1.550 kg   D. 1.860 kg

11. Asgar hiked on two different trails during summer camp. One trail measures 2.863 km.
    Asgar hiked a total of 5.501 km. How long is the other trail?

    A. 3.738 km   B. 3.648 km   C. 2.748 km   **D. 2.638 km**

Metric Relationships

Goal Interpret and compare measurements with different units.

At-Home Help

Length measurements can be compared when they are written in the same units.

For example, to write a length in metres as a length in centimetres, use the fact that 1 m = 100 cm.

3.48 m is the same as 348 cm.

If a problem gives you a shape that has side lengths in different units, write all the measurements you are given in the same unit.

1 cm = 10 mm
1 dam = 10 m
1 m = 100 cm
1 km = 1000 m

1. Rename each measurement using the new unit.

a) 6.04 cm to millimetres
60.4 mm

b) 7.28 km to metres
7280 m

c) 0.591 m to centimetres
59.1 cm

d) 2.006 km to metres
2006 m

e) 4.13 m to centimetres
413 cm

f) 8.9 cm to millimetres
89 mm

2. A playground at a community centre is triangular in shape. Calculate the length of the third side.

0.1500 km

57.4 m

perimeter = 320.2 m

length of two sides = 0.1500 km + 57.4 m
= 150.0 m + 57.4 m
= 207.4 m

length of third side = 320.2 m − 207.4 m
= 112.8 m

3. A box of chocolates is in the shape of a regular hexagon. The side length of the hexagon is 6.2 cm. What is the perimeter of the box?

6.2 cm

perimeter = 6 × 6.2 cm
= 37.2 cm

Perimeters of Polygons

Goal Measure perimeters of polygons and draw polygons with given perimeters.

At-Home Help

Perimeter is the distance around a two-dimensional shape.

To determine the perimeter, measure each side length as accurately as you can using the same unit. Then calculate the sum of the lengths.

For example, for the triangle below,

3.0 cm

3.0 cm

4.5 cm

perimeter
= 4.5 cm + 3.0 cm + 3.0 cm
= 10.5 cm

You will need a ruler.

1. Measure the perimeter of each polygon.

a)

perimeter = 1.6 cm + 2.3 cm + 2.8 cm
= 6.7 cm

b)

perimeter = 2.0 cm + 1.5 cm + 1.8 cm + 3.0 cm
= 8.3 cm

c)

Suggested answer:
perimeter = 6 × 1.4 cm
= 8.4 cm

2. Draw two shapes with the same perimeter as the hexagon in Question 1.

Suggested answer:

2.0 cm   2.4 cm

4.0 cm

2.1 cm

Solve Problems Using Logical Reasoning

Goal Use logical reasoning to solve a problem.

1. a) How many numbers between 100 and 600 have a 3 for at least one of the digits?

At-Home Help

Logical reasoning is a process for using information you have to reach a conclusion.

For example, if you know all the students in a class like ice cream and that Jane is in the class, you can logically reason that Jane likes ice cream.

Suggested answer:

Understand the Problem

I need to find how many numbers between 100 and 600 have one, two, or three 3s in them.

Make a Plan

I can list the numbers between 100 and 199 that have at least one 3. I'll count them. These will be numbers with one or two 3s in them. These will be the same for numbers in the 200s, 400s, and 500s. For the 300s, every number begins with a 3 so I have to count all of them.

Carry Out the Plan

100 to 200	103, 113, 123, 133, 143, 153, 163, 173, 183, 193 130, 131, 132, 134, 135, 136, 137, 138, 139

There are 19 numbers that have a 3 for at least one of the digits between 100 and 199. I multiply by 4 for the 100s, 200s, 400s, and 500s. I add 100 for the 300s.

total = 4 x 19 + 100
      = 76 + 100
      = 176

Look Back

There are 176 numbers between 100 and 600 that have a 3 for at least one of the digits.

b) How many numbers between 100 and 600 have a 7 for at least one of the digits?

The reasoning is the same except there are no numbers that have a 7 in the hundreds place. So I multiply 19 by 5 for the 100s, 200s, 300s, 400s, and 500s.

total = 5 x 19
      = 95

There are 95 numbers between 100 and 600 that have a 7 for at least one of the digits.

Exploring Perimeter

Goal Explore the relationship between perimeter and area measurements.

At-Home Help

Area is a measurement of the amount of space a two-dimensional (2-D) shape covers.

1. Vanessa drew a polygon inside a square.

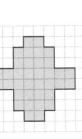

a) Determine the perimeter and the area of the polygon.

perimeter of polygon = 32 units   area of polygon = 36 square units

b) Draw another polygon with the same area but a different perimeter.

Suggested answer:

c) Draw another polygon with the same perimeter but a different area.

Suggested answer:

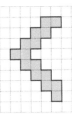

Test Yourself   Page 1

Circle the correct answer.
You will need a ruler.

1. Which unit would be the most appropriate to measure the length of a desk?

   A. millimetres
   B. centimetres
   C. metres
   D. kilometres

2. Which measurement is the same as 0.51 km?

   A. 51 m
   B. 510 m
   C. 5100 cm
   D. 510 000 cm

3. Which measurement is *not* the same as 407 m?

   A. 407 000 mm
   B. 40 700 cm
   C. 4.07 km
   D. 0.407 km

4. What is the length of the fourth side?

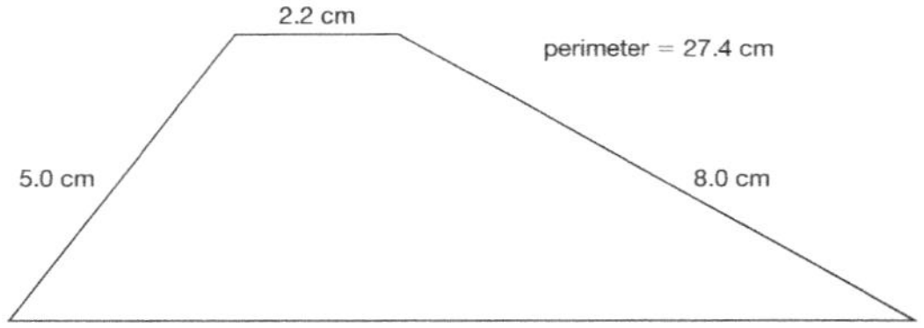

   perimeter = 27.4 cm

   8.0 cm
   2.2 cm
   5.0 cm

   A. 12.2 cm
   B. 12.3 cm
   C. 12.4 cm
   D. 12.5 cm

Test Yourself   Page 2

5. Patrick drew these polygons actual size. Which polygon has a perimeter of 7.5 cm?

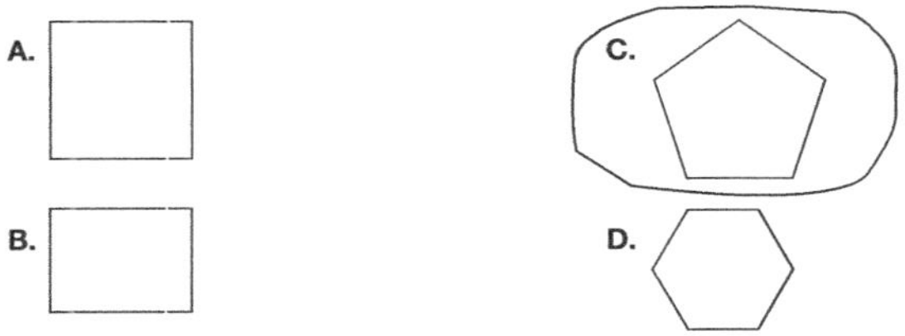

   A.

   B.

   C.

   D.

6. What is the perimeter of the polygon shown below?

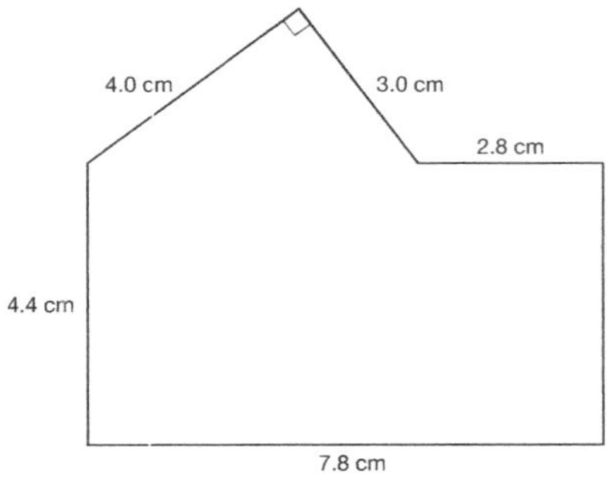

   3.0 cm
   2.8 cm
   4.0 cm
   4.4 cm
   7.8 cm

   A. 25.8 cm
   B. 26.0 cm
   C. 26.2 cm
   D. 26.4 cm

7. The perimeters of two squares differ by 4.0 cm. The sum of the perimeters for the two squares is 16.0 cm. What is the side length of the larger square?

   A. 1.0 cm
   B. 1.5 cm
   C. 2.0 cm
   D. 2.5 cm

8. When the side length of a regular pentagon is increased, its perimeter increases by 12.5 cm. How much longer is the new side length?

   A. 2.0 cm
   B. 2.5 cm
   C. 3.0 cm
   D. 3.5 cm

Page 49

Identify Factors, Primes, and Composites

Goal Identify the factors of prime and composite numbers.

At-Home Help

A **factor** is a whole number that divides another whole number without a remainder.

For example, 2 is a factor of 8 because 2 divides 8 without a remainder.

$8 \div 2 = 4$

The factors of 8 are 1, 2, 4, and 8.

A **prime number** is a number that has only two different factors: 1 and itself.

For example, 2 is a prime number because it has only two factors: 1 and 2.

A **composite number** is a number that has more than two different factors.

For example, 4 is a composite number because it has more than two factors: 1, 2, and 4.

The numbers 0 and 1 are neither prime nor composite.

1. List all the factors of each number.

a) 16
1, 2, 4, 8, 16

d) 22
1, 2, 11, 22

b) 45
1, 3, 5, 9, 15, 45

e) 18
1, 2, 3, 6, 9, 18

c) 31
1, 31

f) 60
1, 2, 3, 4, 5, 6, 10, 12, 15, 20, 30, 60

2. Which numbers are prime and which are composite? Show your work.

a) 41
Prime because the factors of 41 are 1 and 41.

b) 15
Composite because the factors of 15 are 1, 3, 5, and 15.

c) 21
Composite because the factors of 21 are 1, 3, 7, and 21.

d) 12
Composite because the factors of 12 are 1, 2, 3, 4, 6, and 12.

e) 19
Prime because the factors of 19 are 1 and 19.

f) 25
Composite because the factors of 25 are 1, 5, and 25.

Page 50

Identifying Multiples

Goal Solve problems by identifying multiples of whole numbers.

At-Home Help

A **multiple** is a number that is the product of two factors.

For example, 8 is a multiple of 2 because $2 \times 4 = 8$.

To find the multiples of a number, use skip counting or multiplication.

For example:

or $3 \times 1 = 3$
$3 \times 2 = 6$
$3 \times 3 = 9$
$3 \times 4 = 12$
and so on.

The multiples of 3 are 3, 6, 9, 12, ...

1. List five multiples of each number.

a) 4
Suggested answer: 8, 12, 16, 20, and 24

b) 10
Suggested answer: 20, 30, 40, 50, and 60

c) 22
Suggested answer: 44, 66, 88, 110, and 132

d) 9
Suggested answer: 18, 27, 36, 45, and 54

e) 11
Suggested answer: 22, 33, 44, 55, and 66

f) 40
Suggested answer: 80, 120, 160, 200, and 240

2. Sergio has 30 gifts numbered from 1 to 30. There is a kite in each gift with a number that is a multiple of 4. There is a baseball cap in each gift with a number that is a multiple of 6.

a) Which gifts have a kite?
Suggested answer: The multiples of 4 are 4, 8, 12, 16, 20, 24, 28, ...
So gifts with numbers 4, 8, 12, 16, 20, 24, and 28 have a kite.

b) Which gifts have a baseball cap?
Suggested answer: The multiples of 6 are 6, 12, 18, 24, 30, ...
So gifts with numbers 6, 12, 18, 24, and 30 have a baseball cap.

c) Which gifts have both a kite and a baseball cap?
Suggested answer: The multiples 12 and 24 are in the answers for parts **a)** and **b)**.
So gifts with numbers 12 and 24 have both a kite and a baseball cap.

Calculating Coin Values

Goal Use the relationship between coin values to simplify calculations.

1. Zak has 24 quarters in his coin collection. Sketch an array of these coins to calculate 24 × 25.

Suggested answer:
24 × 25 = 600

At-Home Help

Multiplication can be used to calculate the value of coins.

For example, to calculate the value of 12 quarters, multiply 12 × 25. Use an array to make the multiplication easier.

For example, two possible arrays for 12 quarters are

In the first array, the value of each row is 50¢, so the multiplication can be done as 6 × 50 = 300.

In the second array, the value of each column is 100¢, so the multiplication can be done as 3 × 100 = 300. Both arrays show that 12 × 25 = 300¢.

2. Calculate the value of each number of coins.

a) 80 nickels   80 x 5 = 400¢ or $4.00

b) 80 quarters   80 x 25 = 2000¢ or $20.00

c) 50 dimes   50 x 10 = 500¢ or $5.00

3. a) Ramona has 16 nickels, 15 dimes, and 20 quarters. Show one way to arrange each of these coins to calculate the total value of Ramona's coins.
Suggested answer:

b) Calculate the value for each coin arrangement in part a).
(using answer above):

nickels   4 x 20 = 80

dimes   3 x 50 = 150

quarters   5 x 100 = 500

Total: 730¢ or $7.30

Multiplying by Hundreds

Goal Use multiplication facts and regrouping to multiply by hundreds.

1. Calculate.

a) 100 × 40 =   4000

b) 70 × 200 =   14 000

c) 30 × 500 =   15 000

d) 800 × 600 =   480 000

e) 700 × 900 =   630 000

f) 6000 × 60 =   360 000

At-Home Help

To multiply hundreds, you can use regrouping and number facts.

For example, to multiply 200 by 300, you can multiply 200 × 3 × 100.

You can use the number fact 2 × 3 = 6 to calculate 200 × 3 = 600.

Then, to multiply 600 by 100, regroup to a different place value.

600 × 100 = 60 000
So 200 × 300 = 60 000

2. Jake's class baked 20 batches of cookies. Each batch contained 200 cookies. How many cookies did Jake's class bake? Show your work.

20 x 200 = 4000
4000 cookies

3. Marlie needs to fill 400 cups with juice. Each cup holds 200 mL. How much juice does she need? Show your work.

200 x 400 = 80 000
Marlie needs 80 000 mL or 80 L of juice.

Estimating Products

Goal Estimate to check the reasonableness of a calculation.

At-Home Help

To check the reasonableness of a calculation, estimate the answer using one or more mental math strategies.

For example: To check if 57 × 52 = 2964 is reasonable, use rounding or a range.

60 × 50 = 3000
The product 2964 is reasonable.

or 50 × 50 = 2500
60 × 60 = 3600
The answer should be between 2500 and 3600. The product 2964 is reasonable.

1. Check if each answer is reasonable. Use estimation.

a) 64 × 36 = 3204

Not reasonable because 60 × 30 = 1800 and 70 × 40 = 2800. 3204 is not between 1800 and 2800.

b) 122 × 38 = 4636

Reasonable because 100 × 40 = 4000.

c) 44 × 1045 = 66 980

Not reasonable because 40 × 1000 = 40 000 and 50 × 1100 = 55 000. 66 980 is not between 40 000 and 55 000.

d) 78 × 2196 = 171 288

Reasonable because 80 × 2000 = 160 000.

2. **a)** Nirmala rides her bicycle 56 days during the school year. Each of those days, she rides 540 m. Calculate the distance she rides during the school year.

56 × 540 m = 30 240 m

b) Show that your answer is reasonable. Use estimation.

Suggested answer:
I know that 60 × 500 = 30 000. 30 000 is close to 30 240. So my answer is reasonable.

Multiplying by Two-Digit Numbers

Goal Use pencil and paper to multiply a whole number by a two-digit number.

At-Home Help

To multiply a whole number by a two-digit number, you can use regrouping or partial products.

For example:

```
    6 6 5
    1 7 7 6
  ×     1 9
  1 5 9 8 4
  1 7 7 6 0
  3 3 7 4 4
```

or

10	10000	7000	700	60	17 760
9	9000	6300	630	54	15 984
	1000 +	700 +	70 +	6	19 000 + 13300 + 1330 + 114 = 33 744

1. Calculate.

a) 34 × 123

```
    1
    1 2 3
  ×   3 4
    4 9 2
  3 6 9 0
  4 1 8 2
```

c) 81 × 3699

```
    5 7 7
    3 6 9 9
  ×     8 1
    3 6 9 9
  2 9 5 9 2 0
  2 9 9 6 1 9
```

b) 58 × 256

```
    1 4
    2 5 6
  ×   5 8
  2 0 4 8
  1 2 8 0 0
  1 4 8 4 8
```

d) 77 × 6908

```
    6 5
    6 9 0 8
  ×     7 7
  4 8 3 5 6
  4 8 3 5 6 0
  5 3 1 9 1 6
```

2. Rose delivers newspapers in a seniors' residence. She delivers 23 papers on each floor. There are 12 floors in the building. She makes deliveries 15 times per month.

a) Do you think Rose delivers more than 3000 newspapers in a month? Explain how you know.

Suggested answer:
I round all the numbers in the problem to the nearest ten.
20 × 10 = 200 and 200 × 20 = 4000
Since 4000 is greater than 3000, I think Rose delivers more than 3000 newspapers.

b) Calculate the number of newspapers Rose delivers in a month. Show your work.

4140 newspapers

```
    2 3
  ×   1 2
    4 6
  2 3 0
  2 7 6
```

```
    3 3
    2 7 6
  ×   1 5
  1 3 8 0
  2 7 6 0
  4 1 4 0
```

Dividing by 1000 and 10 000

Goal Use mental math to divide whole numbers by 1000 and 10 000.

At-Home Help

To multiply a whole number by 1000, move all digits to the left three places. You can see the pattern by multiplying by 10, 100, or 1000.

For example,

$3 \times 10 = 30$ $13 \times 1000 = 13\,000$

$3 \times 100 = 300$ $130 \times 1000 = 130\,000$

$3 \times 1000 = 3000$ $1300 \times 1000 = 1\,300\,000$

To divide a whole number by 1000, move all digits to the right three places.

For example,

$9000 \div 10 = 900$ $98\,000 \div 1000 = 98$

$9000 \div 100 = 90$ $980\,000 \div 1000 = 980$

$9000 \div 1000 = 9$ $9\,800\,000 \div 1000 = 9800$

1. Calculate. Use mental math.

a) $19\,000 \div 1000 = \underline{19}$

b) $36\,000 \div 1000 = \underline{36}$

c) $2\,080\,000 \div 10\,000 = \underline{208}$

d) $1\,620\,000 \div 1000 = \underline{1620}$

e) $805\,000 \div 1000 = \underline{805}$

f) $40\,000 \div 1000 = \underline{40}$

g) $90\,000 \div 10\,000 = \underline{9}$

h) $6000 \div 1000 = \underline{6}$

2. Leo's binoculars can magnify an object 1000 times.

a) How tall would an object be if the image in the binoculars is 44 000 mm tall?

$44\,000 \div 1000 = 44$

The object would be 44 mm tall.

b) How tall would the image in the binoculars be if the object is 5 mm tall?

$5 \times 1000 = 5000$

The image would be 5000 mm tall.

Dividing by Tens and Hundreds

Goal Use renaming and a division fact to divide by tens and hundreds.

At-Home Help

To divide a whole number by tens or hundreds, you can use renaming.

For example: To divide 60 000 by 200, rename both numbers as hundreds.

$60\,000 = 6$ ten thousands
         $= 60$ thousands
         $= 600$ hundreds

$200 = 2$ hundreds

$60\,000 \div 200$ is the same as 600 hundreds $\div 2$ hundreds.

$600 \div 2 = 300$

So $60\,000 \div 200 = 300$

Check the answer using multiplication.

$300 \times 200 = 60\,000$

1. Calculate. Use multiplication to check each answer.

a) $3000 \div 50 = \underline{60}$

Check:
$60 \times 50 = 3000$

b) $14\,000 \div 200 = \underline{70}$

Check:
$70 \times 200 = 14\,000$

c) $45\,000 \div 300 = \underline{150}$

Check:
$150 \times 300 = 45\,000$

d) $200\,000 \div 400 = \underline{500}$

Check:
$500 \times 400 = 200\,000$

2. a) Kyle and his brother Joe have 24 000 family photos. They saved 600 photos each month. How many months did it take to save the photos?

$24\,000 \div 600 = 40$

It took 40 months.

b) Use multiplication to check your answer.

$40 \times 600 = 24\,000$

Estimating Quotients

Goal Use multiplication and rounding to check the reasonableness of a quotient.

You will need a calculator.

At–Home Help

A **quotient** is the answer to a division question.

For example, 90 is the quotient of 6300 ÷ 70.

6300 ÷ 70 = 90

To check if a quotient is reasonable, you can use rounding and multiplication.

For example, check if 4500 ÷ 24 = 267 is reasonable. If it is reasonable, 4500 should be between 200 × 24 and 300 × 24.

200 × 24 = 4800
300 × 24 = 7200

4500 is not between 4800 and 7200. The quotient should be less than 200. So a quotient of 267 is not reasonable.

1. Check if each answer is reasonable. Use estimation and multiplication.

a) 2170 ÷ 31 = 70

Reasonable. Round 31 to nearest ten.

30 × 70 = 2100, which is close to 2170.

b) 6888 ÷ 28 = 194

Not reasonable because 28 × 100 = 2800 and

28 × 200 = 5600. 6888 is not between 2800 and 5600.

c) 132
58⟌7656

Reasonable. Round 58 and 132 to nearest ten.

60 × 130 = 7800, which is close to 7656.

d) 256
72⟌8280

Not reasonable because 72 × 200 = 14 400. 8280 is less

than 14 400 so the quotient should be less than 200.

2. Choose the best estimate for each quotient.

a) 874 ÷ 26 =   30   10   20   30   **40**

b) 657 ÷ 55 =   10   **10**   10   20   30   40

c) 834 ÷ 44 =   20   10   20   30   **40**

3. The Grade 6 students in Pedro's school are hoping to raise $4000 to buy food for homeless people. There are 84 Grade 6 students in Pedro's school.

a) Calculate the amount of money each student is hoping to raise. Use a calculator.

$4000 ÷ 84 = $47.62

b) Show that your answer is reasonable. Use estimation and multiplication.

Suggested answer: Round 84 and $47.62 to the nearest ten.

50 × 80 = 4000 So my answer is reasonable.

Dividing by Two–Digit Numbers

Goal Divide a four-digit number by a two-digit number.

At–Home Help

To divide a four-digit number by a two-digit number, use estimation and multiplication.

For example: To divide 2365 by 43, round 43 to the nearest ten.

43 is close to 40. Use 40 to estimate.

40 × 50 = 2000 is low.

40 × 60 = 2400 is high but very close.

55
43⟌2365
2150 → 43 × 50 = 2150
 215
 215 → 43 × 5 = 215
   0

To check if a quotient is reasonable, use multiplication or estimation.

For example:

    5 5
  × 4 3
  1 6 5
2 2 0 0
2 3 6 5

Estimate: 60 × 40 = 2400

1. Calculate. Show your work. Check your answers using multiplication.

a) 1088 ÷ 16

      6 8
16⟌1 0 8 8
    9 6 0
    1 2 8
    1 2 8
        0

Check:
        6 8
      × 1 6
      4 0 8
      6 8 0
    1 0 8 8

c) 63⟌4473

      7 1
63⟌4 4 7 3
    4 4 1 0
        6 3
        6 3
          0

Check:
        7 1
      × 6 3
      2 1 3
    4 2 6 0
    4 4 7 3

b) 2278 ÷ 34

      6 7
34⟌2 2 7 8
    2 0 4 0
      2 3 8
      2 3 8
          0

Check:
        6 7
      × 3 4
      2 6 8
    2 0 1 0
    2 2 7 8

d) 81⟌7533

      9 3
81⟌7 5 3 3
    7 2 9 0
      2 4 3
      2 4 3
          0

Check:
        9 3
      × 8 1
        9 3
    7 4 4 0
    7 5 3 3

2. Jamal's class ordered 28 sets of coloured pencils for art projects during the school year. They ordered 1820 pencils altogether.

a) How many coloured pencils are in a set?

65 pencils

      6 5
28⟌1 8 2 0
    1 6 8 0
      1 4 0
      1 4 0
          0

b) Use estimation to check if your answer is reasonable.

Suggested answer: 70 × 30 = 2100

2100 is close to 1820. So my answer of 65 is reasonable.

Communicate About Creating and Solving Problems

Goal Create and explain how to solve multiplication and division problems.

Kiki's family has an energy-efficient washing machine. The machine uses 4620 L of water a year to wash all the laundry. The family washes 7 loads of laundry a month.

1. **a)** Create a multiplication or division problem using the information about Kiki's family.

Suggested answer: How many litres of water does the washing machine use for each load?

b) Explain the solution to your problem in part **a)**. Use the Communication Checklist.

(using answer above):

Understand the Problem
I need to determine the number of litres of water for each load.

Make a Plan
This problem will take more than one step and more than one operation to solve. First I need to multiply 7 by 12 to estimate the number of loads washed in one year. Then I need to divide 4620 by the product to estimate the number of litres used for each load.

Carry Out the Plan
total loads in a year: 7 × 12 = 84 loads
number of litres used for each load: 55 L

$$
\begin{array}{r} 5\ 5 \\ 84\overline{)4\ 6\ 2\ 0} \\ 4\ 2\ 0\ 0 \\ \hline 4\ 2\ 0 \\ 4\ 2\ 0 \\ \hline 0 \end{array}
$$

Look Back
I'll use multiplication to check my answer:

$$
\begin{array}{r} 5\ 5 \\ \times\ 8\ 4 \\ \hline 2\ 2\ 0 \\ 4\ 4\ 0\ 0 \\ \hline 4\ 6\ 2\ 0 \end{array}
$$

The product I get is the same as the total number of litres in the problem. So my answer is reasonable.

Order of Operations

Goal Determine whether the value of an expression changes when the order of calculating changes.

You will need a calculator.

1. Determine the value of each number statement. Using a calculator, enter each number and operation from left to right.

   a) $16 + 12 - 8 = \underline{\ 20\ }$

   b) $9 \times 11 \div 3 = \underline{\ 33\ }$

   c) $16 \div 4 \times 2 + 5 = \underline{\ 13\ }$

   d) $22 - 9 + 12 - 8 = \underline{\ 17\ }$

2. **a)** Sonya entered a contest to win a trip to Mexico. She had to answer this skill-testing question:

   $18 \div 2 + 3 \times 7$

   Show how Sonya could get an answer of 30.

   $18 \div 2 + 3 \times 7$
   $= 9 + 21$
   $= 30$

   b) Drake had to answer this skill-testing question:

   $3 \times 5 - 21 \div 7$

   Show how Drake could get an answer of 12.

   $3 \times 5 - 21 \div 7$
   $= 15 - 3$
   $= 12$

   c) Tilly said the answer to the skill-testing question $45 \div 3 - 7 \times 2$ is 1. Show how she could have got this answer.

   $45 \div 3 - 7 \times 2$
   $= 15 - 14$
   $= 1$

Test Yourself   Page 1

Circle the correct answer.

1. What are the factors of 24?

   A. 1, 24

   B. 1, 2, 4, 6, 12, 24

   C. 1, 2, 3, 4, 6, 8, 12, 24 (circled)

   D. 1, 3, 4, 6, 8, 24

2. Which arrangement best represents 16 × 25?

   A.

   B.

   C. (circled)

   D.

3. During a charity event, 8000 packages of candy were sold. Each package had 40 candies. How many candies were sold?

   A. 12 000 candies

   B. 120 000 candies

   C. 32 000 candies

   D. 320 000 candies (circled)

4. Using estimation, which answer is *not* reasonable?

   A. 68 × 68 = 4624

   B. 82 × 47 = 3854

   C. 312 × 96 = 18 352 (circled)

   D. 23 × 1867 = 42 941

5. Which product is the correct answer to 2481 × 14?

   A. 21 050

   B. 34 734 (circled)

   C. 52 901

   D. 68 437

6. Which quotient is incorrect?

   A. 3600 ÷ 30 = 120

   B. 81 000 ÷ 900 = 90

Test Yourself   Page 2

7. Using estimation and multiplication, which answer is reasonable?

   A. 1998 ÷ 37 = 54 (circled)

   B. 4191 ÷ 33 = 217

   C. $43\overline{)2408}$ = 36

   D. $68\overline{)3196}$ = 67

8. Which quotient is the correct answer to $54\overline{)4698}$?

   A. 87 (circled)

   B. 38

   C. 69

   D. 45

9. Which numbers are multiples of 12?

   A. 35, 36, 40, 45

   B. 24, 48, 60, 72 (circled)

   C. 30, 40, 50, 60

   D. 24, 44, 64, 84

10. What are the answers to 502 000 ÷ 1000 and 14 × 1000?

    A. 5020, 1400

    B. 502, 14

    C. 502, 14 000 (circled)

    D. 5020, 140

11. Mohammed spends 560 min on the Internet each month. How many hours does he spend on the Internet in a year?
    Which explanation is best to solve the problem?

    A. First I need to multiply 560 by 60 to determine the number of hours Mohammed spends in a month. There are 12 months in a year. So I need to multiply the product by 12.

    B. First I need to multiply 560 by 12 to determine the number of minutes Mohammed spends in a year. There are 60 minutes in each hour. So I need to divide the product by 60. (circled)

    C. First I need to divide 560 by 12 to determine the number of minutes Mohammed spends in a year. There are 60 minutes in each hour. So I need to divide the quotient by 60.

    D. First I need to divide 560 by 60 to determine the number of hours Mohammed spends in a month. There are 12 months in a year. So I need to divide the quotient by 12.

Estimating Angle Measures

Goal Compare and estimate angle measures.

You will need a protractor.

1. Estimate the size of each angle.

   a)
   Suggested answer: about 60°

   b)
   Suggested answer: about 80°

   c)
   Suggested answer: about 90°

   d)
   Suggested answer: about 45°

2. Which angles that you know did you use to help you estimate the angles in Question 1? Give reasons for your choices.

   a) *Suggested answer: I used a 60° angle because the angle in part a) looks like it is greater than 45°.*

   b) *Suggested answer: I used a 60° angle because the angle looks like it is greater than the angle in part a).*

   c) *Suggested answer: I used a 90° angle because the angle looks like it is very close to 90°.*

   d) *Suggested answer: I used a 45° angle because the angle looks like it is very close to 45°.*

3. Measure the angles in Question 1. How close were your estimates?

   a) 50°   **c)** 87°

   b) 70°   **d)** 39°

   Suggested answer: All my estimates were within 10° of the actual angle measurements.

Investigating Properties of Triangles

Goal Investigate angle and side relationships of triangles.

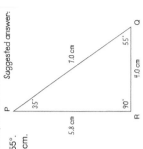
You will need a ruler and a protractor.

1. **a)** Without using a protractor, label these angles on the triangles: 60°, 80°, 20°, 80°, 60°, and 60°.

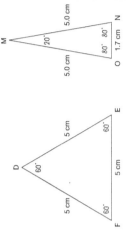

   b) Explain how you know the angle sizes for both triangles.

   Suggested answer: I know that an equilateral triangle has all angles the same size. So the angles must be 60°. I know that an isosceles triangle has two angles that are the same size and the third angle is different. So the two angles that are the same size are 80°. The third angle must be 20°.

   c) Measure the angles with a protractor to check your answer.

2. The angles in triangle PQR are 90°, 35°, and 55°. The side lengths are 5.8 cm, 7.0 cm, and 4.0 cm.

   a) Without using a ruler or protractor, label the angle sizes and side lengths.

   b) Measure the angles and side lengths to check your answers.

   Suggested answer:

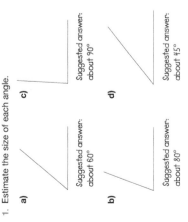

Page 65

Communicate About Triangles

Goal Communicate and explain geometric ideas.

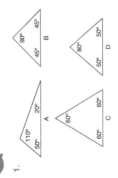
1.

a) Add the angle measures for each triangle.
   A: $110° + 50° + 20° = 180°$
   B: $90° + 45° + 45° = 180°$
   C: $60° + 60° + 60° = 180°$
   D: $50° + 50° + 80° = 180°$

b) Make a hypothesis about the sum of all the angles in a triangle. Use the Communication Checklist.

Suggested answer:
When I add all the angles in a triangle, the sum is always 180°. I think this is always true.

2.

a) Add the angle measures on each line.
   A: $30° + 60° + 90° = 180°$
   B: $25° + 45° + 35° + 75° = 180°$
   C: $105° + 25° + 50° = 180°$
   D: $10° + 40° + 30° + 100° = 180°$

b) Make a hypothesis about the sum of the angles on a straight line. Use the Communication Checklist.

Suggested answer:
When I add all the angles on a straight line, the sum is always 180°. I think this is always true.

Page 66

Constructing Polygons

Goal Construct polygons based on angle measures and side lengths.

You will need a ruler and a protractor.

1. Draw each polygon. Label all side lengths and angle measures.

a) equilateral triangle with side lengths of 3 cm and angle measures of 60°

b) scalene triangle with side lengths of 3 cm, 4 cm, and 5 cm and one angle measure of 90°

c) rectangle with side lengths of 3 cm and 5 cm

d) parallelogram with angle measures of 120° and 60° and side lengths of 4 cm and 5 cm

e) regular hexagon with side lengths of 2 cm and angle measures of 120°

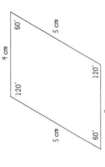

Investigating Properties of Quadrilaterals

Goal Sort and classify quadrilaterals by their properties.

You will need a ruler and a protractor.

1. **a)** Name each quadrilateral.

rectangle

parallelogram

square

kite

quadrilateral

rhombus

trapezoid

b) Draw all the diagonals in each quadrilateral above. Mark any right angles you find where the diagonals meet.

2. Sort the quadrilaterals using a Venn diagram. Choose categories from the property list.

Suggested answer:

Property list
equal diagonals
unequal diagonals
diagonals that meet at 90°
diagonals that do not meet at 90°

Sorting Quadrilaterals

Equal diagonals
rectangle

square

Diagonals that meet at 90°
kite
rhombus

parallelogram   irregular quadrilateral   trapezoid

Sorting Polygons

Goal Sort polygons by line symmetry.

You will need a ruler.

1. **a)** Name each polygon. Draw all the lines of symmetry you can find.

square

rectangle

hexagon

pentagon

trapezoid

isosceles triangle

equilateral triangle

parallelogram

rhombus

scalene triangle

quadrilateral

kite

b) Sort the polygons using a Venn diagram. Choose categories from the property list.

Suggested answer:

Property list
number of lines of symmetry
number of equal sides
number of equal angles
number of sides
number of angles

Sorting Polygons

At least four lines of symmetry

square
pentagon
hexagon

At least two equal sides
equilateral triangle
isosceles triangle
parallelogram
rectangle
kite
rhombus

scalene triangle   quadrilateral   trapezoid

Test Yourself Page 2

Use the polygons below to answer Questions 5 to 7.

5. Which quadrilaterals have equal diagonals?

A. d, e, f   **B.** b, c, g   **C.** b, c, f, g   **D.** a, d, e

6. Which quadrilaterals have diagonals that do not meet at 90°?

A. a, b, d   **B.** a, b, c, d   **C.** c, e, g   **D.** c, e, f, g

7. Which quadrilaterals have diagonals that are unequal but meet at 90°?

A. b, c, d   **B.** c, e   **C.** a, b   **D.** a, f, g

Test Yourself Page 1

Circle the correct answer.

1. Which angles that you know would you use to estimate these angles?

A. 180°, 90°, 45°   **B.** 45°, 120°, 90°   **C.** 45°, 90°, 60°   **D.** 90°, 60°, 60°

2. The side lengths of the triangle are 10 cm and 14 cm. Which side lengths are correct?

A. XZ = 14 cm, XY = 10 cm, YZ = 10 cm
B. XZ = 10 cm, XY = 14 cm, YZ = 10 cm
C. XZ = 14 cm, XY = 14 cm, YZ = 10 cm
D. XZ = 10 cm, XY = 10 cm, YZ = 14 cm

3. Which polygons have more than two lines of symmetry?

A. b, c, f   **B.** a, b, f   **C.** c, d, e, f   **D.** c, e, f

4. What information do you need to construct a regular polygon?

A. all side lengths and all angle measures
B. one side length and one angle measure
C. two side lengths and one angle measure
D. two side lengths and two angle measures

Unit Relationships

Goal Identify relationships between and among linear and square metric units.

At-Home Help

Lengths in metres and centimetres are related.

$1 m = 100 cm$

To express a length in metres as centimetres, you multiply by 100.

For example, 16 m is the same as $16 \times 100 = 1600$ cm.

To express a length in centimetres as metres, you divide by 100.

For example, 240 cm is the same as $240 \div 100 = 2.4$ m.

Areas in square metres and square centimetres are also related.

$1 m^2 = 1 m \times 1 m$
$= 100 cm \times 100 cm$
$= 10 000 cm^2$

To express an area in square metres as square centimetres, you multiply by 10 000.

For example, $7 m^2$ is the same as $7 \times 10 000 = 70 000 cm^2$.

To express an area in square centimetres as square metres, you divide by 10 000.

For example, $1300 cm^2$ is the same as $1300 \div 10 000 = 0.13 m^2$.

1. Express each area in square centimetres.

   a) 8 m² = ___80 000 cm²___   **c)** 3.5 m² = ___35 000 cm²___

   b) 12 m² = ___120 000 cm²___   **d)** 0.7 m² = ___7000 cm²___

2. Express each area in square metres.

   a) 90 000 cm² = ___9 m²___   **c)** 43 000 cm² = ___4.3 m²___

   b) 660 000 cm² = ___66 m²___   **d)** 6000 cm² = ___0.6 m²___

3. Calculate the area of each shape in square centimetres and square metres. Show your work.

   a)

   25 cm, 60 cm

   area = length x width
   = 60 cm x 25 cm
   = 1500 cm²

   area = ___1500___ cm²

   which is the same as ___0.15___ m²

   b)

   8 m, 7 m

   area = length x width
   = 8 m x 7 m
   = 56 m²

   area = ___56___ m²

   which is the same as ___560 000___ cm²

4. Tina made a paper lantern from a 2 m² sheet of paper. She used a 160 cm by 36 cm piece of the paper. What is the area of paper left over?

   area = length x width
   = 160 cm x 36 cm
   = 5760 cm², which is the same as 0.576 m²

   area left over = 2 m² – 0.576 m²
   = 1.424 m²

Area Rule for Parallelograms

Goal Develop and use a rule for calculating the area of a parallelogram.

At-Home Help

A **parallelogram** is a four-sided shape that has two pairs of parallel sides.

To determine the area of a parallelogram, draw a line that is perpendicular to the base. **Perpendicular** means forms a 90° angle. This perpendicular line is the **height** of the parallelogram.

height

base

The general rule for the area of a parallelogram is area = base × height

You will need a ruler and a protractor.

1. Calculate the area of each parallelogram. Show your work.

   a)

   4 cm, 7 cm

   area = base x height
   = 7 cm x 4 cm
   = 28 cm²

   b)

   12 cm, 6 cm

   area = base x height
   = 6 cm x 12 cm
   = 72 cm²

2. Anand drew three parallelograms. Measure the dimensions and calculate the area of each parallelogram. Show your work.

   a)

   area = base x height
   = 2 cm x 3 cm
   = 6 cm²

   b)
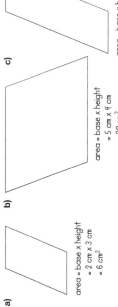

   area = base x height
   = 5 cm x 4 cm
   = 20 cm²

   c)

   area = base x height
   = 2 cm x 5 cm
   = 10 cm²

Area Rule for Triangles

Goal Develop and use a rule for calculating the area of a triangle.

At–Home Help

To determine the area of a triangle, draw a line perpendicular to the base and through the vertex across from it. This perpendicular line is the **height** of the triangle.

To calculate the area of a triangle, multiply the base by the height and divide by 2.

You will need a ruler and a protractor.

1. Calculate the area of each triangle. Show your work.

a)

5 cm
4 cm

area = (base × height) ÷ 2
= (4 cm × 5 cm) ÷ 2
= 20 cm² ÷ 2
= 10 cm²

b)

5 cm
6 cm

area = (base × height) ÷ 2
= (6 cm × 5 cm) ÷ 2
= 30 cm² ÷ 2
= 15 cm²

2. Measure each triangle and calculate the area.

a)

area = (base × height) ÷ 2
= (3 cm × 4 cm) ÷ 2
= 12 cm² ÷ 2
= 6 cm²

b)

area = (base × height) ÷ 2
= (4 cm × 2 cm) ÷ 2
= 8 cm² ÷ 2
= 4 cm²

Geometric Relationships

Goal Identify relationships between triangles and parallelograms.

You will need a ruler.

At–Home Help

Congruent means identical in shape and size.

An **equilateral triangle** has all sides of equal length.

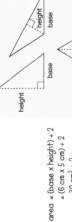

An **isosceles triangle** has two sides of equal length.

A **scalene triangle** has all sides of different lengths.

A **right-angled triangle** has one right angle. A **right angle** measures 90°.

1. Complete the chart by sketching parallelograms made up of two congruent triangles.

Type of triangle	Sketch of parallelograms
equilateral  4 cm, 4 cm, 4 cm	4 cm, 4 cm
isosceles 5 cm, 5 cm, 3 cm	5 cm, 5 cm, 5 cm, 3 cm

2. How is the area of a triangle related to the area of a parallelogram? Explain.

Suggested answer:

Each parallelogram is made up of two identical triangles.
So the area of one triangle is equal to half the area of the parallelogram.

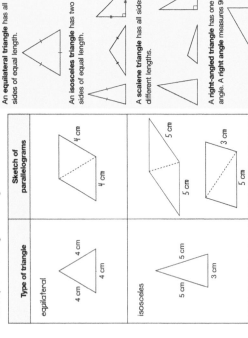

Page 75

Solve Problems Using Open Sentences

Goal Use open sentences to solve problems.

1. Penelope made a fabric flower using triangles. Each petal has a base of 5 cm and a height of 8 cm. She wants to make another flower with twice the area. What base and height could she use for the new petals? Write an open sentence to solve the problem. Show your work.

Suggested answer:

area of one original petal = base × height ÷ 2
= 5 cm × 8 cm ÷ 2
= 20 cm²

area of one new petal
= 20 cm² × 2
= 40 cm²

possible base of triangle = 10 cm
(10 cm × ☐) ÷ 2 = 40 cm²
I know that 80 ÷ 2 = 40 and 10 × 8 = 80.
So the height is 8 cm.

The possible dimensions of the triangle is a base of 10 cm with a height of 8 cm.

2. Matt's house has a basement room with an area of 92 m². Matt's parents are planning to build a bathroom in the room. The area of the room will then be 88 m². List two possible sets of whole number dimensions and shapes for the bathroom. Write an open sentence to solve the problem. Show your work.

Suggested answer: area of bathroom = 92 m² − 88 m²
= 4 m²

The bathroom could be a square or a rectangle.

area = length × width
4 m² = ☐ × ☐
4 m² = 2 m × 2 m
4 m² = 1 m × 4 m

Possible dimensions of the bathroom are a 2 m by 2 m square or a 1 m by 4 m rectangle.

At-Home Help

To solve a problem involving area, use the problem-solving model.

Understand the Problem
- Draw a sketch to help you visualize the problem. Label any dimensions you are given on the sketch.
- Determine what you are asked to find.

Make a Plan
- Use mathematical relationships that can help you solve the problem. For example, to find the area of a parallelogram, use area = base × height.
- Write an open sentence if possible. For example, ☐ × 8 = 96 is an open sentence.

Carry Out the Plan
- You can guess, estimate, or use number facts to solve the open sentence. For example, from the 8 times table, 12 × 8 = 96. So the missing number in the open sentence above is 12.

Look Back
- Check that your answer makes sense with the information in the problem.
- Remember to include the appropriate units in your answer.

Page 76

Areas of Polygons

Goal Calculate the area of polygons by breaking them into simpler shapes.

You will need a ruler.

1. Justin drew a boat using different polygons. Calculate the area of the shape. Show your work.

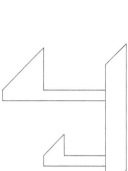

Suggested answer:

area of small sail = (base × height) ÷ 2
= (1 cm × 1 cm) ÷ 2
= 1 cm² ÷ 2
= 0.5 cm²

area of large sail = (base × height) ÷ 2
= (2 cm × 2 cm) ÷ 2
= 4 cm² ÷ 2
= 2 cm²

area of small mast = length × width
= 3 cm × 0.5 cm
= 1.5 cm²

area of large mast = length × width
= 5 cm × 0.5 cm
= 2.5 cm²

area of bottom of boat = base × height
= 6 cm × 1 cm
= 6 cm²

total area = 0.5 cm² + 2 cm² + 1.5 cm² + 2.5 cm² + 6 cm²
= 12.5 cm²

At-Home Help

The area of a complex shape can sometimes be determined by dividing it into several smaller parts. The total area is equal to the sum of the areas of the smaller parts.

For example, to determine the area of the shape above, divide it into five triangles.

area of triangle = (base × height) ÷ 2
= (2 cm × 1 cm) ÷ 2
= 1 cm²

total area = 5 × area of triangle
= 5 × 1 cm²
= 5 cm²

Test Yourself Page 2

6. Which area relationship is *not* true?

A. Two congruent triangles can be used to form a parallelogram. The area of one triangle is half the area of the parallelogram.

B. A parallelogram can be used to form a rectangle if it is cut along its height. The area of the parallelogram is equal to the area of the rectangle.

C. The area of a rectangle is equal to the length times the width.

D. Two congruent triangles can be used to form a parallelogram. The area of one triangle is double the area of the parallelogram.

7. What is the area of the triangle?

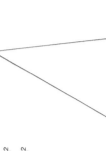

A. 10 cm²   **C.** 20 cm²

B. 12 cm²   **D.** 24 cm²

8. Nadia designed a logo using different polygons. What is the area of the logo?

A. 14 cm²   **C.** 22 cm²

B. 15 cm²   **D.** 36 cm²

Test Yourself Page 1

Circle the correct answer.
You will need a ruler.

1. Which measurement is the same as 13 m²?

A. 1300 cm²   **C.** 130 000 cm²

B. 13 000 cm²   **D.** 1 300 000 cm²

2. Which measurement is the same as 20 000 cm²?

A. 0.2 m²   **C.** 20 m²

B. 2 m²   **D.** 200 m²

3. Which statement is *not* correct?

A. 80 000 cm² is the same as 8 m².

B. 0.1 m² is the same as 10 000 cm².

C. 2500 cm² is the same as 0.25 m².

D. 31 m² is the same as 310 000 cm².

4. What is the area of the parallelogram in square centimetres?

4 cm
8 cm

A. 12 cm²   **C.** 32 cm²

B. 16 cm²   **D.** 36 cm²

5. How many different parallelograms can you make using these triangles?

3 cm 3 cm
2 cm

3 cm 3 cm
2 cm

A. 1   **C.** 3

B. 2   **D.** 4

Page 79

Estimating Products

 Goal Estimate products of decimal tenths and money amounts using a variety of strategies.

1. Estimate each product. Show your work.

a) 3.6 × $29.55
Suggested answer:
4 × $30 = $120 or
3 × $30 plus $\frac{2}{3}$ of $30
= $90 + $20
= $110

b) 2.4 × $16.59
Suggested answer:
3 × $16 = $48 or
2 × $16 plus $\frac{1}{2}$ of $16
= $32 + $8
= $40

c) 4.3 × $18.86
Suggested answer:
4 × $20 = $80 or
4 × $18 plus $\frac{1}{3}$ of $18
= $72 + $6
= $78

d) 5.7 × $12.77
Suggested answer:
6 × $12 = $72 or
5 × $12 plus $\frac{3}{4}$ of $12
= $60 + $9
= $69

e) 6.6 × $24.41
Suggested answer:
7 × $25 = $175 or
6 × $24 plus $\frac{2}{3}$ of $24
= $144 + $16
= $160

f) 8.4 × $49.48
Suggested answer:
8 × $50 = $400 or
8 × $50 plus $\frac{1}{2}$ of $50
= $400 + $25
= $425

2. Estimate each cost. Use a method that will give the answer closest to the actual cost.

a) 1.2 kg at $16.88 per kilogram
Suggested answer:
1 × $17 = $17

b) 0.6 kg at $21.77 per kilogram
Suggested answer:
$\frac{2}{3}$ of $21 = $14

c) 1.8 kg at $18.45 per kilogram
Suggested answer:
2 × $18 = $36

d) 4.3 kg at $29.10 per kilogram
Suggested answer:
4 × $30 plus $\frac{1}{3}$ of $30
= $120 + $10
= $130

e) 5.4 kg at $31.74 per kilogram
Suggested answer:
5 × $32 plus $\frac{1}{2}$ of $32
= $160 + $16
= $176

f) 8.7 kg at $39.25 per kilogram
Suggested answer:
8 × $40 plus $\frac{3}{4}$ of $40
= $320 + $30
= $350

At-Home Help

There are several ways to estimate the cost of an item.

For example, to estimate the cost of 1.3 kg of salmon that costs $17.61 per kilogram, use one of these methods.

1 × $20 = $20 or
1 × $18 plus $\frac{1}{3}$ of $18
= $18 + $6
= $24

Use rounding or numbers that are easier to work with.

Page 80

Multiplying by 1000 and 10 000

 Goal Multiply decimal tenths, hundredths, and thousandths by 1000 and 10 000.

1. Calculate.

a) 1000 × 0.501 = _501_

b) 14.82 × 1000 = _14 820_

c) 10 000 × 29.086 = _290 860_

d) 5.8 × 10 000 = _58 000_

e) 1000 × 67.3 = _67 300_

f) 4.01 × 1000 = _4010_

2. Determine the distance in metres.

a) 51.42 km = _51 420_ m

b) 0.986 km = _986_ m

c) 8.023 km = _8023_ m

d) 18.7 km = _18 700_ m

e) 30.002 km = _30 002_ m

f) 84.06 km = _84 060_ m

3. Jamie rides 4.26 km on his bicycle each day. About how far does he ride in 3 years?
Suggested answer:
One year has about 300 days.
So 3 years have about 1000 days.
I estimate 4.26 km × 1000 = 4260 km.

4. Dana walks about 0.76 m in each step. How far could she travel if she takes 10 000 steps?
0.76 m × 10 000 = 7600 m

At-Home Help

To multiply a decimal tenth, hundredth, or thousandth by 1000, move all digits to the left three places. To multiply by 10 000, move all digits to the left four places. You can see the pattern by multiplying by 10, 100, 1000, or 10 000.

For example,
29.8 × 10 = 298
29.8 × 100 = 2980
29.8 × 1000 = 29 800
29.8 × 10 000 = 298 000

Page 81

Multiplying Tenths by Whole Numbers

 Goal Multiply decimal tenths by whole numbers using models, drawings, and symbols.

At-Home Help

To multiply a decimal tenth by a whole number, you can use regrouping or partial products.
For example:

```
  2 2
 3 5 . 6
 ×     4
 1 4 2 . 4
```

or

```
   2 3
 8 2 4 tenths
 ×       9
 7 4 1 6 tenths
 = 1 4 2 . 4
```

1. Multiply. Show your work.

a) 14.3 × 5

```
 2 1
 1 4 . 3
 ×     5
 7 1 . 5
```

c) 20.7 × 3

```
   2
 2 0 . 7
 ×     3
 6 2 . 1
```

b) 2.8 × 6

Suggested answer:

```
    4
 2 8 tenths
 ×     6
 1 6 8 tenths
 = 16.8
```

d) 82.4 × 9

Suggested answer:

```
   2 3
 8 2 4 tenths
 ×       9
 7 4 1 6 tenths
 = 1 4 2 . 4
```

2. A fruit pie uses 1.3 kg of peaches, 50.5 g of ground almonds, and 2 packages of ricotta. Serina needs to make 4 pies for a family gathering.

a) How much of each ingredient is needed?

Suggested answer:

peaches
```
  1
 1 . 3 kg
 ×     4
 5 . 2 kg
```

almonds
```
   2
 5 0 . 5 g
 ×       4
 2 0 2 . 0 g
```

ricotta
```
 2 packages
 ×     4
 8 packages
```

b) One kilogram of peaches costs $6. What is the total cost of the peaches needed?

Suggested answer:

```
  1
 5 . 2
 ×   6
 31.2
```

The total cost of the peaches is $31.20.

Page 82

Multiplying by 0.1, 0.01, or 0.001

 Goal Multiply by 0.1, 0.01, or 0.001 using mental math.

At-Home Help

To multiply a whole number by 0.1, 0.01, or 0.001, move the digits to the right.

For example,
```
298 × 10 000 = 2 980 000
298 × 1000 = 298 000
298 × 100 = 29 800
298 × 10 = 2980
298 × 1 = 298
298 × 0.1 = 29.8
298 × 0.01 = 2.98
298 × 0.001 = 0.298
```

1. Multiply.

a) 245 × 0.01 = _2.45_

b) 312 × 0.1 = _31.2_

c) 405 × 0.001 = _0.405_

d) 67 × 0.01 = _0.67_

e) 89 × 0.001 = _0.089_

f) 42 × 0.1 = _4.2_

g) 540 × 0.01 = _5.4_

h) 30 × 0.001 = _0.03_

2. Determine the missing measurement.

a) 45 g = _0.045_ kg

b) 57 mm = _5.7_ cm

c) 62 cm = _0.62_ m

d) 202 m = _0.202_ km

e) 368 g = _0.368_ kg

f) 250 mm = _25_ cm

3. What is each measurement?

a) a line of 804 cubes, each 0.01 m long, in metres
8.04 m

b) a line of 62 boxes, each 0.1 m wide, in metres
6.2 m

c) a 480 g bag of sunflower seeds, in kilograms
0.48 kg

d) a 22 g candy, in kilograms
0.022 kg

Multiplying Multiples of Ten by Tenths

Goal Multiply to calculate the decimal portion of a multiple of 10.

1. Calculate. Show your work.

a) $0.3 \times 250 = \underline{\quad 75 \quad}$
Suggested answer:
$0.1 \times 250 = 25$
$3 \times 25 = 75$

b) $0.1 \times 850 = \underline{\quad 85 \quad}$
Suggested answer:
85

c) $0.4 \times 530 = \underline{\quad 212 \quad}$
Suggested answer:
$0.1 \times 530 = 53$
$4 \times 53 = 212$

d) $0.6 \times 800 = \underline{\quad 480 \quad}$
Suggested answer:
$0.1 \times 800 = 80$
$6 \times 80 = 480$

e) $0.5 \times 640 = \underline{\quad 320 \quad}$
Suggested answer:
$0.1 \times 640 = 64$
$5 \times 64 = 320$

f) $0.8 \times 2650 = \underline{\quad 2120 \quad}$
Suggested answer:
$0.1 \times 2650 = 265$
$8 \times 265 = 2120$

2. At Neil's family picnic, 10 people ate 0.6 of 6400 g of roast chicken and 0.5 of a 4500 mL container of potato salad.

a) How much roast chicken did Neil's family eat?
Suggested answer: $0.1 \times 6400 \text{ g} = 640 \text{ g}$
$6 \times 640 \text{ g} = 3840 \text{ g}$

b) How much potato salad did Neil's family eat?
Suggested answer: $0.1 \times 4500 \text{ mL} = 450 \text{ mL}$
$5 \times 450 \text{ mL} = 2250 \text{ mL}$

c) Each person ate the same amount of potato salad. How much potato salad did each person eat?
Suggested answer: $2250 \text{ mL} \div 10 = 225 \text{ mL}$

3. Students from two schools worked at a food bank. One school had 450 students. The other school had 360 students. Eight-tenths of the students in each school participated. How many more students participated from the school of 450 than the school of 360? Suggested answer:

(school of 450) $0.1 \times 450 = 45$ (school of 360) $0.1 \times 360 = 36$
$8 \times 45 = 360$ $8 \times 36 = 288$

difference $= 360 - 288$
$= 72$ students

Communicate About Problem Solving

Goal Explain how to solve problems involving decimal multiplication.

1. Janice exercises for 360 min each week. She walks for 0.6 of the time, and rides her bicycle for the rest of the time.

a) For how many minutes does Janice walk?
Suggested answer:

Understand the Problem
I need to find out how many minutes Janice spends walking.

Make a Plan
I will model 0.6 using a rectangle. 0.6 is the same as $\frac{6}{10}$. So I divide the rectangle into 10 equal parts and shade 6 of them.

360 min

I will determine how many minutes are represented by each part. Then I will multiply that number by 6, because 6 parts are shaded.

Carry Out the Plan
Since 360 is divided into 10 parts, each part represents $360 \div 10 = 36$ min.
6×36 min $= 216$ min
Janice walks for 216 min each week.

b) For how many minutes does Janice ride her bicycle?
Suggested answer:

Understand the Problem
I need to find how many minutes Janice rides her bicycle.

Make a Plan
I know that the total time Janice exercises is 360 min. Since she walks for 216 min, the rest of the time she rides her bicycle. So I need to subtract.

Carry Out the Plan
360 min $- 216$ min $= 144$ min
Janice rides her bicycle for 144 min.

Choosing a Multiplication Method

Goal **Justify the choice of a multiplication method.**

1. Multiply. Did you use mental math, pencil and paper, or a calculator?

a) 0.6 × 5
3
mental math

e) 2.9 × 4
Suggested answer:
2 × 4 = 8
0.9 × 4 = 3.6
8 + 3.6 = 11.6
pencil and paper

b) 1.8 × 9
1.8
× 9
16.2
pencil and paper

f) 5.7 × 100
570
mental math

c) 0.52 × 4
0.52
× 4
2.08
pencil and paper

g) 0.04 × 100
4
mental math

d) 0.37 × 100
37
mental math

h) 0.8 × 7
5.6
mental math

At-Home Help

If numbers are simple to multiply, you can use mental math. Multiplying by 0.001, 0.01, 0.1, 10, 100, and 1000 can be done mentally.

For example, 5.7 × 100 = 570.

If you can multiply numbers without a lot of partial products, use pencil and paper.

For example, 8.2 × 6 = 49.2.

If you have to use a lot of partial products, use a calculator.

For example,
79.523 × 91 = 7236.593.

2. Explain why you chose the method you did for three parts in Question 1.

Suggested answer:
Part a): I used mental math because I know that 6 × 5 = 30. So 0.6 × 5 = 3.
Part b): I used pencil and paper because the numbers were too hard to multiply in my head.
Part e): I used pencil and paper because I had to keep track of the partial products. Then I added the partial products in my head.

Test Yourself   Page 1

Circle the correct answer.

1. Which estimate would be closest to the actual product? 8.3 × 21.20

   A. 8 × 21

   B. 9 × 22

   C. 8 × 21 plus $\frac{1}{3}$ of 21

   D. 9 × 24 plus $\frac{1}{3}$ of 24

2. Which is the best estimate for 0.8 kg at $28.95 per kilogram?

   A. $16   **B.** $18   **C.** $29   **D.** $32

3. What is the product of 1000 and 25.064?

   A. 250.64   **B.** 2506.4   **C.** 25 064   **D.** 250 640

4. What is the product of 0.891 and 1000?

   A. 8.91   **B.** 89.1   **C.** 891   **D.** 8910

5. What is 5.007 km in metres?

   A. 50 007 m   **B.** 50.07 m   **C.** 500.7 m   **D.** 5007 m

6. What is the product of 6.2 and 7?

   A. 42.2   **B.** 43.4   **C.** 44.4   **D.** 42.9

7. What is the product of 503 and 0.01?

   A. 0.503   **B.** 5.03   **C.** 50.3   **D.** 503

8. What is the product of 0.1 and 827?

   A. 8270   **B.** 827   **C.** 8.27   **D.** 82.7

9. One muffin has a mass of 0.025 kg. What is the mass in grams?

   A. 250 g   **B.** 0.25 g   **C.** 2.5 g   **D.** 25 g

10. What is the product of 0.4 and 3260?

   A. 652   **B.** 978   **C.** 1304   **D.** 1448

Test Yourself   Page 2

11. A library has 5460 books. Three-tenths of the books are mysteries. How many mystery books are there?

A. 546 books   **B. 1638 books**   C. 1820 books   D. 2730 books

12. Jason wants to multiply 0.6 by 920. He wrote

$0.1 \times 920 = \boxed{}$

$\boxed{} \times 92 = \boxed{}$

What are the missing numbers?

A. 92, 6, 552   B. 9.2, 6, 55.2   C. 92, 60, 5520   D. 92, 60, 552

13. Lina saved $240 planting trees. She spent 0.4 of that amount on a new jacket. How much did she spend on the jacket?

A. $60   **B. $96**   C. $120   D. $9.60

14. Which product is greatest?

A. 1000 × 0.6   B. 1000 × 0.105   **C. 1000 × 0.92**   D. 1000 × 0.033

15. Mitch bought 0.6 kg of grapes. One kilogram cost $3.00 on sale. The regular price was $4.00 per kilogram. How much did Mitch save?

$ 3.00

A. $1.80   C. $2.40

B. $0.80   **D. $0.60**

Estimating Quotients

Goal Estimate quotients when dividing decimal numbers.

At-Home Help

To estimate a quotient when dividing a decimal number by a one-digit number, use one of these methods.
- Round the decimal number to the nearest whole number.

  For example: 5.9 ÷ 3
  Round 5.9 to 6.
  6 ÷ 3 = 2
  5.9 ÷ 3 is about 2.
- Rename the decimal number.

  For example: 2.8 ÷ 3
  2.8 is close to 2.7, which is an easier number to divide by 3.
  Rename 2.7 as 27 tenths.
  27 tenths ÷ 3 = 9 tenths, or 0.9
  2.8 ÷ 3 is about 0.9.
- Rewrite the division as a multiplication question.
  For example: 7.7 ÷ 6
  6 × □ = 7.7
  6 × 1.0 = 6.0
  6 × 1.1 = 6.6
  6 × 1.5 = 9.0

  7.7 ÷ 6 is between 1.1 and 1.5, or about 1.3.

1. Estimate each quotient. Show your work.

a) 8.4 ÷ 5

Suggested answer: Round 8.4 to 8.0.
Rename 8 ones as 80 tenths.
80 tenths ÷ 5 = 16 tenths
8.4 ÷ 5 is about 1.6.

b) 13.7 ÷ 7

Suggested answer: Round 13.7 to 14.
14 ÷ 7 = 2
13.7 ÷ 7 is about 2.

c) 18.3 ÷ 4

Suggested answer: 4 × □ = 18.3
4 × 4.0 = 16.0
4 × 5.0 = 20.0
4 × 4.5 = 18.0

18.3 ÷ 4 is about 4.5.

d) 24.2 ÷ 3

Suggested answer: Round 24.2 to 24.
24 ÷ 3 = 8
24.2 ÷ 3 is about 8.

2. Ray bought 15.5 m of wire to make four sculptures with equal lengths of wire. Estimate the length of wire for each sculpture.

Suggested answer:
The problem can be solved by calculating 15.5 m ÷ 4.
4 × □ = 15.5
4 × 3.0 = 12.0
4 × 4.0 = 16.0
4 × 3.5 = 14.0
The answer is between 3.5 and 4.0.
15.5 m ÷ 4 is about 3.75.
Ray needs about 3.75 m of wire for each sculpture.

Dividing Money

Goal Solve problems by dividing money.

You will need a calculator.

1. Use a calculator to divide. Use multiplication to check your answers.

a) $27.84 ÷ 3 = _____ $9.28

$9.28
× 3
$27.84

b) $36.85 ÷ 5 = _____ $7.37

$7.37
× 5
$36.85

c) $29.50 ÷ 2 = _____ $14.75

$14.75
× 2
$29.50

d) $45.96 ÷ 6 = _____ $7.66

$7.66
× 6
$45.96

e) $51.66 ÷ 7 = _____ $7.38

$7.38
× 7
$51.66

At-Home Help

To solve division problems involving money, use multiplication or estimation to check your answers.

For example: Four friends share the cost of three books equally. The books cost $26.99, $22.99, and $16.99. What is the cost for each person?

(total cost)
$26.99 + $22.99 + $16.99 = $66.97
$66.97 ÷ 4 = $16.74

Check by multiplying:
22 1
$16.74
× 4
$66.96

Check by estimating:
Estimated total cost:
$27 + $23 + $17 = $67
Estimated cost per person:
67 ÷ 4 is close to 68 ÷ 4 = 17, or about $17

2. Lara and two friends bought a book for $28.95, a pizza for $22.99, and a game for $26.85. Each person paid the same amount.

a) What was the cost for each person? Use a calculator.

Suggested answer: (total cost)
$28.95
22.99
+ 26.85
$78.79

$78.79 ÷ 3 = $26.26

b) Use estimation to show that your answer is reasonable.

Suggested answer: Estimated total cost: 30 + 23 + 27 = 80
Estimated cost per person: 80 ÷ 3 is close to 81 ÷ 3 = 27
My estimate of $27 is close to $26.26. So my answer is reasonable.

Dividing Decimals by One-Digit Numbers

Goal Express quotients as decimal numbers to tenths.

1. Divide. Check two answers using multiplication.

a) 23.4 ÷ 3
7.8
3)23.4
21
2.4
2.4
0

d) 6)37.2
6.2
6)37.2
36
1.2
1.2
0

b) 30.4 ÷ 4
7.6
4)30.4
28
2.4
2.4
0

e) 44.5 ÷ 5
8.9
5)44.5
40
4.5
4.5
0
8.9
× 5
44.5

c) 7)41.3
5.9
7)41.3
35
6.3
6.3
0
5.9
× 7
41.3

f) 8)25.6
3.2
8)25.6
24
1.6
1.6
0

At-Home Help

To divide a decimal tenth by a whole number, use the same procedure as dividing two whole numbers.

For example:
8.5
9)76.5
72 → 9 × 8 = 72
4.5 → 9 × 0.5 = 4.5
0

To check if a quotient is reasonable, use multiplication or estimation.

For example:
4
8.5
× 9
76.5

Estimate:
8 × 10 = 80 or 80 ÷ 10 = 8

2. Sheila has 3.0 kg of raisins. She keeps one-half for herself. She divides the remaining amount equally among three friends. How many kilograms of raisins does each person get? Show your work.

Suggested answer:
(Sheila) 3.0 kg ÷ 2 = 1.5 kg
(each friend) 1.5 kg ÷ 3 = 0.5 kg
0.5
3)1.5
1.5
0.0

Dividing by 10, 100, 1000, and 10 000

Goal Divide whole and decimal numbers by 10, 100, 1000, and 10 000 using mental math.

1. Calculate. Use mental math.

a) 321 ÷ 100 = _3.21_

b) 25 ÷ 10 = _2.5_

c) 4.5 ÷ 10 = _0.45_

d) 321 ÷ 10 000 = _0.0321_

e) 18 ÷ 1000 = _0.018_

f) 60.7 ÷ 100 = _0.607_

g) 58 240 ÷ 1000 = _58.24_

h) 58 240 ÷ 10 000 = _5.824_

2. Chris has 12.3 L of juice. He wants to pour equal amounts of juice into 10 glasses. How many litres of juice will be in each glass?

Suggested answer:
12.3 L ÷ 10 = 1.23 L

3. 56.2 kg of rice is divided equally into 100 containers. How many kilograms of rice are in each container?

Suggested answer:
56.2 kg ÷ 100 = 0.562 kg

4. Concert organizers ordered 3550 L of water for an audience of 10 000 people. How many millilitres of water will be available for each person?

Suggested answer:
3550 L ÷ 10 000 = 0.355 L
0.355 × 1000 = 355 mL

Solving Problems by Working Backward

Goal Use a working-backward strategy to solve problems.

Lynne has 17.2 m of ribbon to wrap two sizes of gifts. There are four small gifts and one larger gift. She needs 4.8 m to wrap the larger gift. How much ribbon does she need to wrap each smaller gift?

Suggested answer:

Understand the Problem
I need to determine the length of ribbon for each of the smaller gifts. I know the total length of ribbon and the length needed for the larger gift.

Make a Plan
I'll draw a diagram to represent the problem.

17.2 m

| ? | ? | ? | ? | 4.8 m |

The diagram shows four lengths of ribbon added to the length of 4.8 m. The total length is 17.2 m. I can work backward to estimate and calculate the length needed for each of the four small gifts.

Carry Out the Plan
I estimate the length needed for each small gift is greater than 3 m.

Step 1: I subtract the length used for the larger gift from the total length. The length needed for all four smaller gifts is 12.4 m.

Step 2: I divide the length needed for the four gifts to determine the length for each gift.
12.4 m ÷ 4 = 3.1 m

The length needed for each of the smaller gifts is 3.1 m.

Test Yourself

Circle the correct answer.

1. Which quotient is the closest estimate for 14.6 ÷ 3?

   A. 4   **(B.)** 5   **C.** 6   **D.** 7

2. Miranda got 4.94 when she divided 34.58 by 7. Which method is incorrect to use to check her answer?

   (A.) Multiply 34.58 by 4.94.   **C.** Round 4.94 to 5. Then multiply by 7.

   B. Multiply 4.94 by 7.   **D.** Use a calculator to divide 34.58 by 7.

3. Which quotient answers the question $46.32 ÷ 4?

   (A.) $11.58   **B.** $11.98   **C.** $12.58   **D.** $12.98

4. Royce and four friends bought a book and a game. The book cost $16.99 and the game cost $24.96. Each paid the same amount. What was the cost for each person?

   A. $11.39   **B.** $10.75   **C.** $10.48   **(D.)** $8.39

5. Yvette paid $26.08 for eight different flags. Each flag cost the same amount. How much did each flag cost?

   A. $2.61   **B.** $3.00   **(C.)** $3.26   **D.** $3.50

6. What is the quotient of 67.2 ÷ 3?

   A. 21.8   **(B.)** 22.4   **C.** 24.3   **D.** 25.4

7. Nigel bought 4.5 kg of trail mix. He kept 2 kg for himself. He divided the remaining amount equally among five friends. How many kilograms of trail mix did each friend get?

   A. 0.3 kg   **B.** 0.4 kg   **(C.)** 0.5 kg   **D.** 0.6 kg

8. Which quotient is incorrect?

   A. 40.3 ÷ 10 = 4.03   **(C.)** 3.5 ÷ 100 = 0.35

   B. 690 ÷ 1000 = 0.69   **D.** 7 ÷ 1000 = 0.007

9. 20.4 L of fruit punch is divided equally into 100 containers. How many litres of punch are in each container?

   A. 204 L   **B.** 2.04 L   **(C.)** 0.204 L   **D.** 0.024 L

10. Nemil added 0.6 years to his age, and divided that result by 4. The final answer was 2.4. How old is Nemil?

   A. 8   **(B.)** 9   **C.** 10   **D.** 11

Visualizing and Constructing Polyhedrons

Goal Visualize and build polyhedrons from 2-D nets.

At-Home Help

A **polyhedron** is a closed three-dimensional shape with polygons as faces. Pyramids and prisms are two kinds of polyhedrons.

For example:

pyramid

prism

net of pyramid

net of prism

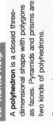

A.

B.

C.

D.

1. Which are nets of pyramids? How can you tell?

   nets A and D

   Suggested answer: Pyramids have triangular faces, except for the base. Both these nets have triangles.

2. Which are nets of prisms? How can you tell?

   nets B and C

   Suggested answer: Prisms have rectangular faces, except for the top and base. Both these nets have rectangles.

3. What nets can you make from these shapes? Sketch each net and name the polyhedron it would make.

   square-based pyramid

   hexagonal prism

   cube

   hexagonal prism

   rectangular prism

   hexagonal pyramid

Volume of Rectangular and Triangular Prisms

Goal Calculate the volume of rectangular and triangular prisms.

1. Determine the volume of each rectangular prism.

a) *Suggested answer:*
   area of base
   = length × width
   = 5 cm × 6 cm
   = 30 cm²

   volume of prism
   = area of base × height
   = 30 cm² × 4 cm
   = 120 cm³

b) *Suggested answer:*
   volume of prism
   = length × width × height
   = 7 cm × 3 cm × 9 cm
   = 189 cm³

2. Determine the volume of each triangular prism.

a) *Suggested answer:*
   volume of prism = area of base × height
   = (4 cm × 5 cm ÷ 2) × 8 cm
   = 10 cm² × 8 cm
   = 80 cm³

b) *Suggested answer:*
   volume of prism = area of base × height
   = (6 m × 3 m ÷ 2) × 5 m
   = 9 m² × 5 m
   = 45 m³

Surface Area of Polyhedrons

Goal Determine the surface area of triangular and rectangular prisms.

1. a) Sketch a net for the triangular prism. Label the dimensions.
   Suggested answer:

   b) Determine the surface area of the triangular prism.
   area of prism = area of 2 triangles + area of one 7 cm by 6 cm rectangle + area of two 7 cm by 5 cm rectangles
   = 2 × (6 cm × 4 cm ÷ 2) + (7cm × 6 cm) + 2 × (7 cm × 5 cm)
   = 24 cm² + 42 cm² + 70 cm²
   = 136 cm²

2. a) Sketch a net for the rectangular prism. Label the dimensions.

   b) Determine the surface area of the rectangular prism.
   area of prism = area of two 5 cm by 9 cm rectangles + area of two 8 cm by 9 cm rectangles + area of two 5 cm by 8 cm rectangles
   = 2 × (9 cm × 5 cm) + 2 × (9 cm × 8 cm) + 2 × (8 cm × 5 cm)
   = 2 × 45 cm² + 2 × 72 cm² + 2 × 40 cm²
   = 90 cm² + 144 cm² + 80 cm²
   = 314 cm²

Solve Problems by Making a Model

Goal Make models to solve problems.

You will need centimetre cubes.

1. Jared is building rectangular prisms with 12 centimetre cubes.

a) Which prism has the least surface area?

Suggested answer:

Understand the Problem

I need to determine the dimensions of the rectangular prism with the least surface area.

Make a Plan

I'll model the prism using 12 centimetre cubes.
I'll make rectangular prisms with the cubes and calculate the surface area of each one.
I'll record my results in a chart.

Carry Out the Plan

Prism	Surface area
	surface area = 50 cm²
	surface area = 40 cm²
	surface area = 38 cm²
	surface area = 32 cm²

The prism that is 3 cm long, 2 cm wide, and 2 cm high has the least surface area.
The surface area of this prism is 32 cm².

b) What is the volume of the prism in part **a)**?

Suggested answer: volume of prism = length × width × height
= 3 cm × 2 cm × 2 cm
= 12 cm³

Creating Isometric Sketches

Goal Sketch a polyhedron built from cubes.

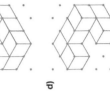
a)

b)

c)

d)

1. Sketch each structure.

a)

b)

c)

d)

Creating Cube Structures from Sketches

Goal Create cube structures based on an isometric sketch.

You will need linking cubes or other cube-shaped objects for building.

At-Home Help

It is possible to build cube structures based on isometric drawings.

For example, the isometric drawings below represent a cube structure.

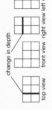

Two cube structures that match the drawing would be

In order to know exactly how many cubes to use, you need more than one drawing to show what the cube structure looks like.

1. **a)** Build a cube structure based on the isometric drawing. How many cubes did you use?

___7___ cubes

b) Sketch at least two views of your cube structure so someone else could build it exactly as you did.

Suggested answer:

2. **a)** Build another cube structure using more cubes than you used in Question 1.

How many cubes did you use? ___8___ cubes

b) Sketch at least two views of your cube structure so someone else could build it exactly as you did.

Suggested answer:

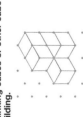

Different Views of a Cube Structure

Goal Draw top, front, right, and side views of a cube structure.

At-Home Help

Cube structures can be represented accurately if their top, front, and side views are shown.

For example, the cube structure above can be represented by top, front, and side views.

change in depth

top view   front view   right view   left view

1. Sketch the top, front, right, and left views of this cube structure.

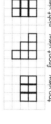

top view   front view   right view   left view

2. **a)** Sketch the top, front, right, and left views of this cube structure.

top view   front view   right view   left view

b) Why is it important to include both side views?

Suggested answer: The right view shows changes in depth, which means there are steps. If you don't draw the left view, you might think that there are steps on that side too. The structure does not have any changes in depth on the left view. So the left view looks different from the right view.

Creating Cube Structures from Different Views

Goal **Make cube structures when given their top, front, and side views.**

You will need linking cubes or other cube-shaped objects for building.

top view   front view   right view   left view

At-Home Help

A cube structure can be constructed when its top, front, and side views are given.

For example, if you are given these views, you can build the appropriate cube structure.

top view   front view   right view   left view

1. **a)** Make three different cube structures that match the top view. *Suggested answer:*

b) Make three different cube structures that match the right view. Do any of your cube structures match both the top and right views?

Suggested answer:

None of my cube structures for part b) has a top view that matches.

c) Make several different cube structures that match the front view. Do any of your cube structures match all four views?

Suggested answer:

Yes, my first structure in part c) matches all four views.

Test Yourself   Page 1

Circle the correct answer.
Use the polygons below to answer Questions 1 and 2.

1. Which combination of shapes would make a pyramid?

   A. 3 triangles, 1 square
   B. 4 triangles, 1 rectangle
   C. 5 triangles, 1 hexagon
   D. 6 triangles, 1 hexagon

2. Which combination of shapes would *not* make a prism?

   A. 2 hexagons, 3 rectangles, 3 squares
   B. 2 hexagons, 6 rectangles
   C. 2 triangles, 3 rectangles
   D. 2 triangles, 3 squares

Use the prism below to answer Questions 3 and 4.

4 cm   5 cm   6 cm

3. What is the surface area of the rectangular prism?

   A. 74 cm^2 **B.** 120 cm^2 **C.** 148 cm^2 **D.** 240 cm^2

4. What is the volume of the rectangular prism?

   A. 74 cm^3 **B.** 120 cm^3 **C.** 148 cm^3 **D.** 240 cm^3

Test Yourself   Page 2

Use the prism below to answer Questions 5 and 6.

20 cm
9 cm
16 cm
12 cm

5. What is the surface area of the triangular prism?

A. 624 cm²   B. 424 cm²   C. 570 cm²   D. 1040 cm²

6. What is the volume of the triangular prism?

A. 960 cm³   B. 2800 cm³   **C. 864 cm³**   D. 2240 cm³

7. All of the cube structures below are made with seven cubes. Which ones are the same?

a

b

c

d

e

f

A. a, d   **B. b, c**   C. b, e   D. a, f

8. Which top, front, and side views match cube structure c in Question 7?

A.

top view   front view   side view

B.

top view   front view   side view

C.

top view   front view   side view

D.

top view   front view   side view

Comparing and Ordering Fractions

Goal   Compare and order fractions on number lines.

1. Compare. Write >, <, or =.

0    $\frac{1}{2}$ 1 $1\frac{1}{2}$ 2 $2\frac{1}{2}$ 3

a) $\frac{4}{3}$ $\boxed{>}$ $\frac{2}{3}$

b) $\frac{2}{5}$ $\boxed{=}$ $\frac{4}{10}$

c) $\frac{7}{4}$ $\boxed{>}$ $\frac{3}{8}$

d) $1\frac{1}{3}$ $\boxed{<}$ $1\frac{4}{6}$

e) $1\frac{3}{4}$ $\boxed{<}$ $2\frac{1}{2}$

f) $2\frac{1}{5}$ $\boxed{>}$ $2\frac{1}{10}$

2. Order each set of numbers from least to greatest. Use a number line.

a) $\frac{3}{8}$, $1\frac{1}{4}$, $\frac{3}{4}$, $\frac{5}{8}$

$\frac{3}{8}$ $\frac{5}{8}$ $\frac{3}{4}$ 1 $1\frac{1}{4}$ 2

$\frac{3}{8}$, $\frac{5}{8}$, $\frac{3}{4}$, $1\frac{1}{4}$

b) $2\frac{1}{3}$, $1\frac{2}{3}$, $\frac{8}{3}$, $1\frac{3}{6}$

1 $1\frac{3}{6}$ $1\frac{2}{3}$ 2 $2\frac{1}{3}$ $\frac{8}{3}$ 3

$1\frac{3}{6}$, $1\frac{2}{3}$, $2\frac{1}{3}$, $\frac{8}{3}$

c) $\frac{4}{4}$, $1\frac{1}{8}$, $\frac{2}{4}$, $\frac{7}{4}$, $1\frac{5}{8}$

0 $\frac{2}{4}$ 1 $1\frac{1}{8}$ $1\frac{5}{8}$ $1\frac{7}{8}$ $\frac{7}{4}$ 2

$\frac{2}{4}$, $\frac{4}{4}$, $1\frac{1}{8}$, $1\frac{5}{8}$, $\frac{7}{4}$

d) $\frac{5}{6}$, $\frac{2}{3}$, $1\frac{1}{6}$, $\frac{1}{3}$, $\frac{6}{3}$

$\frac{1}{6}$ $\frac{2}{3}$ $\frac{5}{6}$ 1 $1\frac{1}{3}$ 2 $\frac{6}{3}$

$\frac{1}{6}$, $\frac{2}{3}$, $\frac{5}{6}$, $1\frac{1}{6}$, $\frac{6}{3}$

Comparing Fractions with Unlike Denominators

Goal Compare fractions when the denominators are different.

1. Compare. Write >, <, or =.

a) $\frac{1}{3}$ < $\frac{4}{5}$

b) $\frac{2}{5}$ < $\frac{1}{2}$

c) $\frac{3}{8}$ > $\frac{1}{3}$

d) $\frac{3}{4}$ > $\frac{2}{3}$

e) $\frac{6}{10}$ = $\frac{3}{5}$

f) $\frac{1}{2}$ > $\frac{5}{8}$

2. Which amount is greater? Tell how you know.

a) $\frac{1}{3}$ or $\frac{3}{8}$ of a bag of popcorn

Suggested answer:
I used grid paper to draw a number line. I chose a whole with 24 sections.
$\frac{3}{8}$ is past $\frac{1}{3}$ on the number line.

$\frac{3}{8}$

b) $\frac{2}{5}$ or $\frac{2}{3}$ of a container of juice

Suggested answer:
The numerators are the same, so the fraction with the lower denominator is greater.

$\frac{2}{3}$

c) $\frac{5}{7}$ or $\frac{1}{2}$ of a length of string

Suggested answer:
I used grid paper to draw a number line. I chose a whole with 14 sections.
$\frac{5}{7}$ is past $\frac{1}{2}$ on the number line.

$\frac{5}{7}$

Fraction and Decimal Equivalents

Goal Relate fractions to decimals and determine equivalents.

1. Write an equivalent fraction for each decimal.

a) $0.34 = \frac{34}{100}$

b) $0.6 = \frac{6}{10}$

c) $0.07 = \frac{7}{100}$

d) $1.3 = 1\frac{3}{10}$

e) $2.37 = 2\frac{37}{100}$

f) $3.04 = 3\frac{4}{100}$

2. Explain how to write $\frac{4}{5}$ as a decimal.

Suggested answer:
I could divide a rectangle into 10 equal sections.

If I shade 4 rows, that represents $\frac{4}{5}$.
$\frac{4}{5}$ of the rectangle is 8 sections.
So $\frac{4}{5}$ is the same as 0.8.

Equivalent Ratios

Goal Determine equivalent ratios and use them to solve problems.

1. Determine the missing number to make an equivalent ratio.

a) 5 to 8 = 10 to 16

b) 12 : 100 = 3 : 25

c) 21 to 33 = 7 to 11

d) 18 : 6 = 9 : 3

e) 75 : 24 = 25 : 8

f) 24 to 60 = 2 to 5

2. Kenton makes salsa by mixing tomatoes and peppers in a ratio of 5 : 2.

a) Write ratios equivalent to 5 : 2 in the ratio table.

Tomatoes	5	10	15	20	25	30
Peppers	2	4	6	8	10	12

b) If Kenton has 40 tomatoes, how many peppers does he need?

5 : 2 = 40 : 16
16 peppers

c) If Kenton has 20 peppers, how many tomatoes does he need?

5 : 2 = 50 : 20
50 tomatoes

3. Stacy makes one batch of muffins using muffin mix and water in a ratio of 3 : 1. She needs to make 4 batches for school. How many cups of muffin mix will she need?

3 : 1 = 12 : 4
12 cups of muffin mix

Ratios

Goal Identify and model ratios to describe situations.

1. Write the ratio of grey items to white items.

a) 5 : 6

b) 2 : 5

c) 8 : 3

d) 0 : 6

2. Write the ratio of white to grey for each situation in Question 1.

a) 6 : 5

b) 5 : 2

c) 3 : 8

d) 6 : 0

3. a) What is the ratio of oats to raisins?
3 : 2

b) What is the ratio of coconut to oats?
1 : 3

c) What is the ratio of raisins to coconut?
2 : 1

3 parts oats
1 part coconut
2 parts raisins

Percents as Special Ratios

Goal Understand the meaning of percent.

1. Write each as a ratio, a fraction, and a percent.

a) 10 to 25

$10 : 25$
$\dfrac{10}{25} = \dfrac{40}{100}$
$= 40\%$

b) 0.07

$7 : 100$
$\dfrac{7}{100} = 7\%$

c) 13 out of 20

$13 : 20$
$\dfrac{13}{20} = \dfrac{65}{100}$
$= 65\%$

d) 0.18

$18 : 100$
$\dfrac{18}{100} = 18\%$

2. Write each ratio as an equivalent fraction with a denominator of 100, a decimal, and a percent.

a) $\dfrac{9}{20}$

$\dfrac{9}{20} = \dfrac{45}{100}$
$= 0.45$
$= 45\%$

b) $\dfrac{33}{50}$

$\dfrac{33}{50} = \dfrac{66}{100}$
$= 0.66$
$= 66\%$

c) 2 out of 5

$\dfrac{2}{5} = \dfrac{40}{100}$
$= 0.40$
$= 40\%$

d) 8 out of 25

$\dfrac{8}{25} = \dfrac{32}{100}$
$= 0.32$
$= 32\%$

3. A survey at Jennifer's school showed that 19 out of 25 students chose pizza as their favourite lunch food.

a) What percent of students chose pizza?

$19 \text{ out of } 25 = 19 : 25$
$= \dfrac{19}{25}$
$= \dfrac{76}{100}$
$= 76\%$

b) What percent of students did not choose pizza?

Suggested answer: Out of 25 students, 25 − 19 = 6 students did not choose pizza.

$6 \text{ out of } 25 = 6 : 25$
$= \dfrac{6}{25}$
$= \dfrac{24}{100}$
$= 24\%$

Relating Percents to Decimals and Fractions

Goal Compare and order percents, fractions, and decimals.

1. Write each number as a percent. Order the numbers from least to greatest.

a) 0.6, $\dfrac{7}{10}$, 0.07, $\dfrac{8}{20}$

$0.6 = \dfrac{6}{10}$ $\dfrac{7}{10} = \dfrac{70}{100}$ $0.07 = \dfrac{7}{100}$ $\dfrac{8}{20} = \dfrac{40}{100}$
$= \dfrac{60}{100}$ $= 70\%$ $= 7\%$ $= 40\%$
$= 60\%$

Order is 7%, 40%, 60%, 70% or 0.07, $\frac{8}{20}$, 0.6, $\frac{7}{10}$.

b) $\dfrac{4}{5}$, 0.12, $\dfrac{16}{25}$, 0.85

$\dfrac{4}{5} = \dfrac{80}{100}$ $0.12 = \dfrac{12}{100}$ $\dfrac{16}{25} = \dfrac{64}{100}$ $0.85 = \dfrac{85}{100}$
$= 80\%$ $= 12\%$ $= 64\%$ $= 85\%$

Order is 12%, 64%, 80%, 85% or 0.12, $\frac{16}{25}$, $\frac{4}{5}$, 0.85.

2. An art show has paintings, sculptures, and sketches. Thirty-five percent of the items are paintings and 0.13 of the items are sketches. What fraction of the items are sculptures?

Suggested answer:
35% paintings

$0.13 = \dfrac{13}{100}$
$= 13\%$ sketches

Percent of sculptures $= 100\% - (35\% + 13\%)$
$= 100\% - 48\%$
$= 52\%$

$52\% = \dfrac{52}{100}$
$= \dfrac{13}{25}$

The fraction of items that are sculptures is $\dfrac{13}{25}$.

Estimating and Calculating Percents

Goal **Estimate and calculate percents.**

1. Estimate the percent of each number. Show your work.

a) 40% of 180

Suggested answer:
50% of 180 is half of 180, or 90.
So 40% of 180 is a little less than 90 or about 75.

b) 30% of 90

Suggested answer:
10% of 90 is 9.
30% of 90 is 9 × 3 = 27.

c) 50% of 412

Suggested answer:
50% of 412 is half of 412, or about 200.

d) 75% of 208

Suggested answer:
50% of 208 is half of 208, or about 100.
25% of 208 is about half of 100, or 50.
So 75% of 208 is about 100 + 50 = 150.

2. A store has a sign saying, "15% off all jackets." Kenny wants to buy a leather jacket that has a regular price of $360. About how much will Kenny save?

Suggested answer:
25% of $360 is $\frac{1}{4}$ of $360, or $90.
15% is about halfway between 0 and 25% but closer to 25%. So 15% of $360 is about half of $90, or about $50.
So Kenny will save about $50.

Unit Rates

Goal **Represent relationships using unit rates.**

1. Calculate the unit rate for each item.

a) 5 guitar picks for $1.00

Suggested answer: 20¢/pick

b) 2 CDs for $15.00

Suggested answer:
2 : 15 = 1 : ☐
☐ = 7.5
$7.50/CD

c) 8 mini-muffins for $2.40

Suggested answer: 30¢/muffin

d) 3 tickets for $3.00

Suggested answer:
3 : 3 = 1 : ☐
☐ = 1
$1.00/ticket

2. **a)** What is the price of one scoop of each type of ice cream?

Suggested answer:
(vanilla) 3 : 150¢ = 1 : ☐
☐ = 50
50¢/scoop

(chocolate) 2 : 140¢ = 1 : ☐
☐ = 70
70¢/scoop

(mango) 4 : 4 = 1 : ☐
☐ = 1
$1.00/scoop

(strawberry) 4 : 360¢ = 1 : ☐
☐ = 90
90¢/scoop

b) Which ice cream is the least expensive?
vanilla

c) Which ice cream is the most expensive?
mango

> **Ice cream**
>
> Vanilla
> 3 scoops for $1.50
>
> Chocolate
> 2 scoops for $1.40
>
> Mango
> 4 scoops for $4.00
>
> Strawberry
> 4 scoops for $3.60

Solving Problems Using Guess and Test

Goal Use a guess and test strategy to solve problems.

The ratio of flowers to herbs in Babak's garden is 6 : 2. He started with 80 plants. He wants to increase the number of herbs in his garden so that 40% of his plants are herbs. How many more herb plants must he get?

At-Home Help
Sometimes using a guess and test strategy is a good way to solve a problem.
Use a chart to help you organize the information you are given and what you want to calculate.
Remember to check if your answer is reasonable after guessing.

Suggested answer:

Understand the Problem
Babak started with 80 plants that made 100% of his garden. If Babak had 8 plants, 6 of them would be flowers and 2 would be herbs.

0%   25%   50%   75%   100%
0   20   40   60   80

Make a Plan
I'll set up a chart and use a guess and test strategy to determine how many more herb plants Babak needs.

Carry Out the Plan

Guess	Number of flowers	Number of herbs	Total number of flowers and herbs	Percent of herbs
start with	60	20	80	$\frac{20}{80} = \frac{1}{4} = 25\%$
add 10 herbs	60	30	90	$\frac{30}{90} = \frac{1}{3}$ on about 30%
add 20 herbs	60	40	100	$\frac{40}{100} = 40\%$

Look Back
Babak will need 20 more herb plants to make his garden have 40% herbs.
I'll check if my answer is correct Babak started with 80 plants.
If he adds 20 plants, then he will have 80 + 20 = 100 plants altogether.
40% of 100 is 40. So he should have 60 flowers and 40 herbs.
He started out with 20 herbs. So 20 more herb plants will give 40 herb plants.

Copyright © 2017 by Nelson Education Ltd.

Test Yourself   Page 1

Circle the correct answer.

1. Which fraction is greatest?
$\frac{4}{5}, \frac{2}{3}, \frac{3}{4}, \frac{3}{8}$
A. $\frac{4}{5}$ (circled)
B. $\frac{2}{3}$
C. $\frac{3}{4}$
D. $\frac{3}{8}$

2. What is the correct order of these fractions from least to greatest?
$\frac{2}{3}, \frac{1}{6}, 1\frac{1}{5}, \frac{7}{8}, \frac{2}{5}$
A. $\frac{2}{5}, \frac{1}{3}, \frac{2}{6}, \frac{7}{8}, 1\frac{1}{5}$
B. $\frac{1}{6}, \frac{2}{5}, \frac{2}{3}, \frac{7}{8}, 1\frac{1}{5}$ (circled)
C. $\frac{1}{6}, \frac{2}{3}, \frac{2}{5}, \frac{7}{8}, 1\frac{1}{5}$
D. $\frac{2}{3}, \frac{2}{5}, \frac{1}{6}, \frac{7}{8}, 1\frac{1}{5}$

3. What is 1.03 as a fraction?
A. $\frac{13}{100}$
B. $1\frac{3}{10}$
C. $1\frac{3}{100}$ (circled)
D. $\frac{103}{1000}$

4. What is the ratio of white counters to grey counters?
A. 4 : 3
B. 3 : 7
C. 4 : 7
D. 3 : 4 (circled)

5. Which ratios are equivalent to 6 out of 15?
i) 2 : 5   ii) 3 out of 10   iii) 4 out of 10   iv) 10 : 25   v) 20 : 45
A. i, ii, iii
B. ii, iv, v
C. i, iii, iv (circled)
D. ii, iii, iv

6. What is the correct order of these numbers from least to greatest?
$\frac{8}{25}, 0.14, 30\%, \frac{2}{5}, 8\%, 0.09$
A. 8%, 0.09, 0.14, 30%, $\frac{8}{25}, \frac{2}{5}$ (circled)
B. 0.09, 0.14, $\frac{2}{5}, \frac{8}{25}$, 8%, 30%
C. 0.09, $\frac{2}{5}$, 0.14, $\frac{8}{25}$, 8%, 30%
D. 8%, 0.09, $\frac{2}{5}$, 0.14, $\frac{8}{25}$, 30%

Test Yourself   Page 2

7. What is 0.3 as a ratio, a fraction, and a percent?

   A. 3 : 100, $\frac{3}{100}$, 30%

   B. 3 : 10, $\frac{3}{10}$, 30%

   C. 3 : 10, $\frac{3}{10}$, 3%

   D. 3 : 10, $\frac{3}{100}$, 3%

8. What is $\frac{12}{25}$ as an equivalent fraction with a denominator of 100, a decimal, and a percent?

   A. $\frac{12}{100}$, 0.12, 12%

   B. $\frac{40}{100}$, 0.4, 40%

   C. $\frac{48}{100}$, 0.48, 48%

   D. $\frac{16}{100}$, 0.16, 16%

9. What is the best estimate for 25% of 212?

   A. about 30   B. about 40   **C. about 50**   D. about 60

10. Which type of muffin is the least expensive?

    A. cinnamon raisin

    B. maple pecan

    C. cranberry orange

    D. crunchy oat

    ### Muffins
Blueberry bran	5 for $3.50
Cranberry orange	6 for $3.60
Crunchy oat	8 for $3.20
Maple pecan	3 for $2.70
Cinnamon raisin	5 for $2.50

11. A brand of light cheese says "20% less fat" on the label. The regular version of the cheese has 85 g of fat. About how many fewer grams of fat are in the light cheese?

    A. about 10 g   **B. about 20 g**   C. about 30 g   D. about 40 g

---

Conducting Probability Experiments

Goal Compare probabilities in two experiments.

Game 1
1. Place a shuffled deck of cards face down.
2. Turn over the top card.
3. If the card is an ace, you get 4 points.

A player wins if he or she has at least 10 points after 4 turns.

Game 2
1. Place a shuffled deck of cards face down.
2. Turn over the top card.
3. If the card is a red card (heart or diamond), you get 2 points.

A player wins if she or he has at least 6 points after 4 turns.

> **At-Home Help**
>
> **Probability** refers to the likelihood that an event will happen.
>
> For example, if you flip a coin, there are two possible outcomes. You can get either heads or tails.
>
> The probability of getting heads is the same as the probability of getting tails.

1. Predict which game you are more likely to win. Justify your prediction.

   Suggested answer: I think I'm more likely to get a red card than an ace. There are only 4 aces in the deck, but there are 26 red cards. I think I'm more likely to win Game 2.

2. Tammy played both games three times. Which game are you more likely to win? Use probability language to explain why.

Game 1

Turn number	1	2	3	4	Points
Ace?	×	×	×	✓	4

Turn number	1	2	3	4	
Ace?	×	×	×	×	4

Turn number	1	2	3	4	
Ace?	×	×	×	×	0

Game 2

Turn number	1	2	3	4	Points
Red card?	✓	✓	×	✓	6

Turn number	1	2	3	4	
Red card?	×	✓	✓	✓	6

Turn number	1	2	3	4	
Red card?	✓	×	✓	✓	6

Suggested answer: You're more likely to win Game 2. Tammy won Game 2 three times but lost Game 1 every time. For Tammy to win Game 1, she would have to turn over 3 aces. Since there are only 4 aces in the deck of 52, getting 3 of them would be very unlikely.

For Tammy to win Game 2, she would have to turn over 3 red cards. Since there are 26 red cards in the deck of 52, it is more likely that Tammy can flip 3 of them to win.

Using Percents to Describe Probabilities

Goal Conduct experiments and use percent to describe probabilities.

1. Siegfried rolled a die 20 times.

Roll	1	2	3	4	5	6	7	8	9	10
Number on die	2	3	1	4	2	6	3	5	2	1

Roll	11	12	13	14	15	16	17	18	19	20
Number on die	5	3	1	2	6	4	1	3	2	4

Record the probability of each event as a percent.

a) rolling a 1
$\frac{4}{20} = \frac{20}{100}$
$= 20\%$

b) rolling a multiple of 3
$\frac{6}{20} = \frac{30}{100}$
$= 30\%$

c) rolling an odd number
$\frac{10}{20} = \frac{50}{100}$
$= 50\%$

d) rolling a 7
$\frac{0}{20} = \frac{0}{100}$
$= 0\%$

2. The probability of winning a game is 40%. Predict how many times you expect to win in each situation.

a) if you play 10 times
$\frac{40}{100} = \frac{4}{10}$
4 times

b) if you play 25 times
$\frac{40}{100} = \frac{10}{25}$
10 times

c) if you play 50 times
$\frac{40}{100} = \frac{20}{50}$
20 times

3. a) Roll a die 25 times and record each roll.

Suggested answer:

Roll	1	2	3	4	5	6	7	8	9	10	11	12	13	14	15	16	17	18	19	20	21	22	23	24	25
Number on die	2	1	3	4	2	5	1	6	3	2	1	3	4	5	2	1	6	4	2	3	5	4	1	6	2

b) Record each probability as a percent.

i) rolling an even number
$\frac{13}{25} = \frac{52}{100}$
$= 52\%$

ii) rolling a number less than 5
$\frac{19}{25} = \frac{76}{100}$
$= 76\%$

iii) rolling a number less than 10
$\frac{25}{25} = \frac{100}{100}$
$= 100\%$

Solving a Problem by Conducting an Experiment

Goal Use an experiment as a problem solving strategy.

Jessica and her brother use a die to decide who will help with dinner each night. An even number means it is Jessica's turn. An odd number means it is her brother's turn. Conduct an experiment to determine the probability that Jessica will help with dinner more than 3 times in the next week.

Suggested answer:

Understand the Problem
I need to calculate the fraction of the days that Jessica will help with dinner in a week.

Make a Plan
I'll conduct an experiment. I'll roll a die 7 times. Each roll represents a day of the week. I'll record the results of each roll in a chart.

I'll do the experiment 20 times and see what fraction of the days Jessica will help with dinner. If I get more than 3 even numbers in an experiment, Jessica will help with dinner more than 3 times that week.

Carry Out the Plan
These are my results.

Experiment	1	2	3	4	5	6	7	8	9	10	11	12	13	14	15	16	17	18	19	20
Roll 1	2	6	1	4	5	6	3	5	3	2	4	5	1	2	6	2	1	3	4	3
Roll 2	1	5	1	2	1	2	5	3	2	3	4	1	3	1	2	1	3	4	2	5
Roll 3	3	2	4	1	2	3	1	5	2	5	2	3	1	3	5	3	4	1	4	3
Roll 4	5	4	3	1	6	3	6	1	5	1	4	1	3	5	4	3	3	5	3	2
Roll 5	4	2	2	1	5	2	4	6	2	6	5	4	3	4	6	5	5	3	5	3
Roll 6	6	3	2	5	6	3	3	4	5	5	4	6	5	4	6	1	6	5	6	2
Roll 7	1	1	5	2	5	4	1	2	1	2	5	2	1	6	1	2	1	2	2	4
	✓			✓		✓		✓		✓		✓		✓		✓				✓

I got more than 3 even numbers in 9 of the 20 experiments. So the probability of Jessica helping with dinner more than 3 times in a week is $\frac{9}{20}$. That is equivalent to $\frac{45}{100}$ or 45%.

Look Back
There are 3 even numbers and 3 odd numbers on a die. So if I roll a die, there is a 3 in 6 chance of getting an even number. If I roll a die 7 times, I expect to get an even number either 3 or 4 times. My result of 45% looks reasonable.

Theoretical Probability

Goal Create a list of all possible outcomes to determine a probability.

1. If you shuffle a deck of cards, what is the theoretical probability of each event?

a) picking an ace $\frac{4}{52}$ or $\frac{1}{13}$

c) picking a face card $\frac{12}{52}$ or $\frac{3}{13}$

b) picking a spade $\frac{13}{52}$ or $\frac{1}{4}$

2. If you roll a die two times, what is the theoretical probability of each event?

a) sum of 6 $\frac{5}{36}$

Roll 2 \ Roll 1	1	2	3	4	5	6
1	2	3	4	5	⑥	7
2	3	4	5	⑥	7	8
3	4	5	⑥	7	8	9
4	5	⑥	7	8	9	10
5	⑥	7	8	9	10	11
6	7	8	9	10	11	12

b) sum of 10 $\frac{3}{36}$ or $\frac{1}{12}$

c) difference of 5 $\frac{2}{36}$ or $\frac{1}{18}$

Roll 2 \ Roll 1	1	2	3	4	5	6
1	0	1	2	3	4	⑤
2	1	0	1	2	3	4
3	2	1	0	1	2	3
4	3	2	1	0	1	2
5	4	3	2	1	0	1
6	⑤	4	3	2	1	0

d) difference of 2 $\frac{8}{36}$ or $\frac{2}{9}$

3. Imagine spinning this spinner twice.

a) What is the theoretical probability that the sum of the two spins is greater than 4? $\frac{10}{16}$ or $\frac{5}{8}$

b) What is the theoretical probability that the sum is an odd number? $\frac{8}{16}$ or $\frac{1}{2}$

Spin 2 \ Spin 1	1	2	3	4
1	2	3	4	⑤
2	3	4	⑤	⑥
3	4	⑤	⑥	⑦
4	⑤	⑥	⑦	⑧

Tree Diagrams

Goal Use a tree diagram to determine a theoretical probability.

1. a) Use a tree diagram to list the possible outcomes if this spinner is spun twice.

Spin 1	Spin 2
2	2, 3, 4
3	2, 3, 4
4	2, 3, 4

b) Determine the theoretical probability that the difference of the numbers is 0. $\frac{3}{9}$ or $\frac{1}{3}$

Tree diagram for parts b) and c):

Spin 1	Spin 2	Difference	Product
2	2	0	4
	3	1	6
	4	2	8
3	2	1	6
	3	0	9
	4	1	12
4	2	2	8
	3	1	12
	4	0	16

c) Determine the theoretical probability that the product of the numbers is greater than 6. $\frac{6}{9}$ or $\frac{2}{3}$

2. Nathan and Jay are playing a game with the spinner in Question 1. Nathan wins if his two spins give a sum greater than 5. Otherwise, Jay wins. Use a tree diagram to explain if this game is fair.

Suggested answer: The theoretical probability of getting a sum greater than 5 is $\frac{6}{9}$ or $\frac{2}{3}$. A game is fair if each player has an equal chance of winning. If there are two players, each player should have a 50% chance of winning. In this game, Nathan is more likely to get a sum greater than 5. So the game is not fair.

Spin 1	Spin 2	Sum
2	2	4
	3	5
	4	6
3	2	5
	3	6
	4	7
4	2	6
	3	7
	4	8

Comparing Theoretical and Experimental Probability

Goal Compare the theoretical probability of an event with the results of an experiment.

1. Two green marbles, two blue marbles, and one yellow marble are placed in a bag. The marbles are mixed up and two marbles are picked, one at a time, without looking.

a) What is the theoretical probability of picking a green marble and then a yellow one? Use a tree diagram.

Tree diagram for parts a) and b):

1st marble	2nd marble	Experimental results
G1	G2	1
	B1	2
	B2	2
	Y	1 ✓
G2	G1	3
	B2	1
	Y	
B1	G1	1
	G2	1
	B2	1
	Y	1 ✓
B2	G1	1
	G2	1
	B1	1
	Y	
Y	G1	1
	G2	2
	B1	
	B2	1

Suggested answer: $\frac{1}{20}$

$\frac{2}{20}$ or $\frac{1}{10}$

b) Conduct an experiment 20 times. What is your experimental probability for this event? Record your results beside your tree diagram in part **a)**.

c) Why might the experimental probability be different from the theoretical probability?

Suggested answer: The experimental probability was different because I only did the experiment 20 times. Also, I might not have mixed up the marbles well enough between experiments.

At–Home Help

To determine the theoretical probability of an event, you can use a tree diagram to list all possible outcomes.

To determine the experimental probability of that event, conduct an experiment.

Before comparing theoretical and experimental probabilities, make sure the experiment was conducted many times.

Usually experimental probabilities are not the same as theoretical probabilities. If you do a great enough number of experiments, the experimental probability will be the same as or very close to the theoretical one.

Test Yourself   Page 1

Circle the correct answer.
Use the chart to answer Questions 1 and 2.

Nazir's Rolls of a Die

First 5 rolls	2	1	6	3	5
Next 5 rolls	1	1	4	2	5
Next 5 rolls	3	2	4	5	1

1. What is the probability of Nazir rolling an even number in the first 10 rolls?

   A. $\frac{3}{10}$ **B.** $\frac{4}{10}$ **C.** $\frac{7}{10}$ **D.** $\frac{3}{5}$

2. What is the probability of Nazir rolling a number greater than 4 in all 15 rolls?

   A. $\frac{4}{15}$ **B.** $\frac{1}{3}$ **C.** $\frac{7}{15}$ **D.** $\frac{11}{15}$

3. What is the theoretical probability of spinning blue on this spinner?

   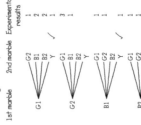

   A. $\frac{1}{6}$ **B.** $\frac{2}{6}$ **C.** $\frac{2}{3}$ **D.** $\frac{1}{2}$

4. Renata spun the spinner in Question 3 10 times. What is the probability of Renata spinning blue?

Spin number	1	2	3	4	5	6	7	8	9	10
Colour	blue	yellow	green	red	green	green	purple	blue	blue	red

   A. 10%   **B.** 20%   **C.** 30%   **D.** 40%

5. What is the theoretical probability of flipping a coin three times and getting heads all three times?

   A. $\frac{1}{8}$ **B.** $\frac{1}{4}$ **C.** $\frac{3}{8}$ **D.** $\frac{1}{2}$

6. What is the theoretical probability of picking an ace from a shuffled deck of cards?

   A. $\frac{1}{52}$ **B.** $\frac{4}{52}$ **C.** $\frac{1}{2}$ **D.** $\frac{3}{4}$

---

192   Answers

Page 124

Page 124

Describing Rotations

Goal Perform and describe the rotation of a shape around a centre that is on the shape.

You will need a ruler and a protractor.

At-Home Help

A **rotation** is a turn of a shape. A rotation is described by the centre of rotation, the angle of rotation, and the direction of the turn.

The **centre of rotation** is the point that a shape rotates around. Each point in the shape must stay an equal distance from the centre of rotation.

The **angle of rotation** is how much the shape moved about the centre of rotation. The direction of rotation can be described as clockwise (CW) or counterclockwise (CCW).

For example, the shape below is rotated 90° CW about vertex A.

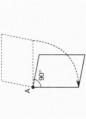

1. Describe the rotation of this shape.

Suggested answer: The black dot on the letter "F" is the centre of rotation. The letter was rotated 90° CCW about the centre of rotation.

2. **a)** Describe how to rotate the letter so that it ends up in the same position.

Suggested answer: I choose the centre of rotation to be at one vertex. If I do two rotations of 180° about the centre of rotation, it will look the same as it was to start with.

b) Describe a rotation that will change how the letter looks. Sketch the rotation.

Suggested answer: If I choose the same centre of rotation and I rotate the letter 90° CCW about the centre of rotation, the letter will be in a different position.

3. Rotate the letter 90° CW several times. What do you notice about the results?

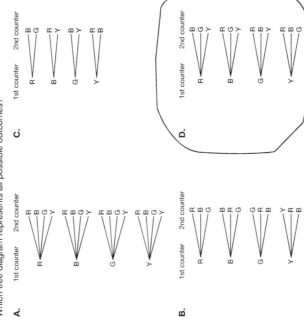

Suggested answer:
I get the same results as the original letter.

Page 123

Test Yourself   Page 2

7. One red counter, one blue counter, one green counter, and one yellow counter are placed in a bag. The counters are mixed up and two counters are picked, one at a time, without looking. Each time a counter is picked, it is not replaced in the bag. Which tree diagram represents all possible outcomes?

A.

1st counter 2nd counter

R — R, B, G, Y
B — R, B, G, Y
G — R, B, G, Y
Y — R, B, G, Y

C.

1st counter 2nd counter

R — B, G, Y
B — R, G, Y
G — B, Y
Y — R, B

B.

1st counter 2nd counter

R — R, B, G
B — B, R, G
G — G, R, B
Y — Y, R, B

D.

1st counter 2nd counter

R — B, G, Y
B — R, G, Y
G — R, B, Y
Y — R, B, G

8. What is the theoretical probability of picking a green counter and a yellow counter (in any order) for the situation in Question 7?

A. $\frac{1}{12}$ **B.** $\frac{2}{12}$ **C.** $\frac{1}{4}$ **D.** $\frac{1}{3}$

Copyright © 2017 by Nelson Education Ltd.

Answers 193

Performing and Measuring Rotations

Goal Perform and describe rotations of shapes about centres not on the shape.

You will need a ruler, scissors, and a protractor.

1. Describe each rotation. Include the centre of rotation, angle, and direction.

At-Home Help

Shapes can be rotated about centres that are not on the shape itself.

For example, this triangle is rotated 90° CCW about point P. Point P is the centre of rotation and is outside the triangle.

90° CCW

a)

Suggested answer:
The rotation is 90° CW about point A.

b)

Suggested answer:
The rotation is 180° CCW about point B.

2. Trace the hexagon and cut it out. Rotate the hexagon 90° CW about point X. Sketch the final position.

90°

Rotational Symmetry

Goal Determine whether and how a shape can be turned to fit on itself.

1. **a)** Predict the order of rotational symmetry for this shape.

At-Home Help

Rotational symmetry exists when a shape can fit on itself exactly more than once in one complete rotation.

For example, a square can fit on itself four times during one complete rotation.

Order of rotational symmetry is the number of times a shape will fit on itself exactly during one complete rotation.

A shape that can fit on itself only once during one complete rotation has no rotational symmetry, but we say that it has an order of rotational symmetry of 1.

A square has an order of rotational symmetry of 4.

square: 4

Suggested answer: I predict that when I rotate the star around its centre, I'll get the same shape five different ways.

b) Trace and cut out the shape. Determine the order of rotational symmetry.

5

2. Name each shape.
List its order of rotational symmetry.

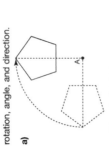
trapezoid: 1

pentagon: 5

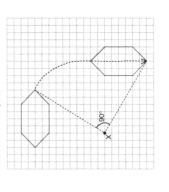
equilateral triangle: 3

parallelogram: 1

Communicate Using Diagrams

Goal Use clear, labelled diagrams to communicate.

You will need a ruler and a protractor.

1. **a)** Melanie said that if you reflect shape K in the line of reflection A, then in the line of reflection B, then in the line of reflection A, then in the line of reflection B, you get the same shape you started with. Draw a diagram to check Melanie's prediction. Use the Communication Checklist.

Suggested answer: My diagram shows that Melanie's prediction is true.

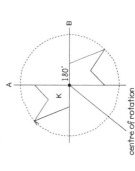

b) What other transformations could you perform on shape K to get the same shape you started with? Draw a diagram to show your transformation(s).
Suggested answer: Rotate K 180° CW and again 180° CW.

Exploring Transformation Patterns with Technology

Goal Relate number patterns to translation, rotation, and reflection patterns.

You will need a ruler.

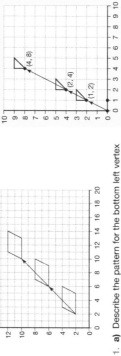

1. **a)** Describe the pattern for the bottom left vertex if the translations continue the same way.

Suggested answer:
The pattern is (2, 2), (6, 6), (10, 10), ...
The pattern rule is start at (2, 2) and add 4 to each coordinate.

b) What would be the 10th term in the pattern?

Suggested answer:
The first term is 2. The common difference is 4.
10th term = 2 + nine 4s
          = 2 + 36
          = 38
The 10th shape will have its bottom left vertex at (38, 38).

Test Yourself   Page 1

Circle the correct answer.

1. What is the best description of this rotation?

A. The triangle is rotated 90° CW.

B. The centre of rotation is A and the angle of rotation is 90°.

C. The triangle is rotated 90° CW about A.

D. The triangle is rotated 90° CCW about A.

2. What is the best description of this rotation?

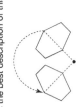

A. The shape is rotated 90° CW.

B. The centre of rotation is X and the angle of rotation is 90°.

C. The shape is rotated 90° CW about X.

D. The shape is rotated 90° CCW about X.

3. What is the order of rotational symmetry of this regular pentagon?

A. 3   B. 4   C. 5   D. 6

Creating Designs

Goal Create a design by performing transformations on a basic shape.

You will need scissors and a protractor.

1. **a)** Trace this shape and cut it out. Create a design by transforming this shape. Use translations, reflections, or rotations.

Suggested answer:

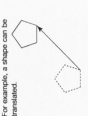

At-Home Help

Designs can be created by transforming a basic shape. For example, a shape can be translated.

A shape can be reflected.

line of reflection

A shape can be rotated.

By performing a series of transformations, you can create a design.

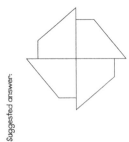

b) Describe the transformations you used.

Suggested answer:
I rotated the shape four times. Each rotation is 90° CCW. The centre of rotation is the bottom right vertex.

c) Can you get the same design by doing different transformations?

Suggested answer:
Yes. I can reflect the shape along the vertical line and then along the horizontal line. That will make the shape at the lower left. I can rotate both shapes 90° CCW to get the third and fourth shapes.

Page 131

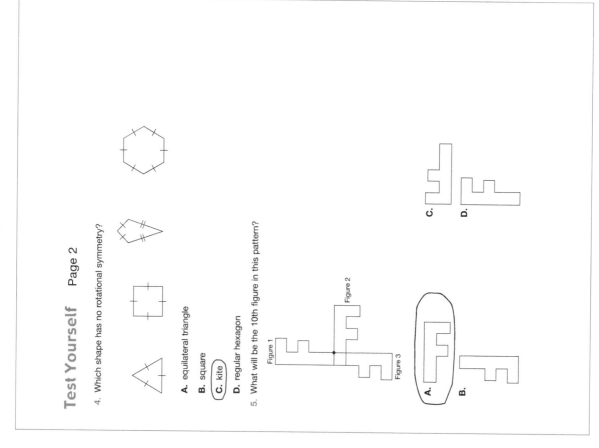

Test Yourself Page 2

4. Which shape has no rotational symmetry?

A. equilateral triangle

B. square

C. kite

D. regular hexagon

5. What will be the 10th figure in this pattern?

Figure 1   Figure 2

Figure 3

A.

B.

C.

D.

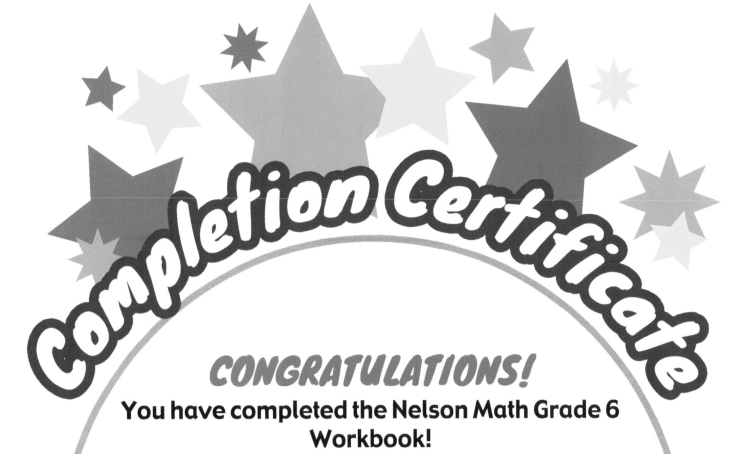

Completion Certificate

CONGRATULATIONS!

You have completed the Nelson Math Grade 6 Workbook!

Presented to: _____

Date: _____

GREAT JOB!

Study Planner

Sunday	Monday	Tuesday	Wednesday	Thursday	Friday	Saturday

Study Topic Checklist

☐ Patterns in Mathematics
☐ Numeration
☐ Data Management
☐ Addition and Subtraction
☐ Measuring Length
☐ Multiplication and Division
☐ 2-D Geometry
☐ Area
☐ Multiplying Decimals
☐ Dividing Decimals
☐ 3-D Geometry and 3-D Measurement
☐ Fractions, Decimals, Ratios, and Percents
☐ Probability
☐ Patterns and Motion in Geometry

Notes

Goals

Study Planner

Sunday	Monday	Tuesday	Wednesday	Thursday	Friday	Saturday

Study Topic Checklist

- ☐ Patterns in Mathematics
- ☐ Numeration
- ☐ Data Management
- ☐ Addition and Subtraction
- ☐ Measuring Length
- ☐ Multiplication and Division
- ☐ 2-D Geometry
- ☐ Area
- ☐ Multiplying Decimals
- ☐ Dividing Decimals
- ☐ 3-D Geometry and 3-D Measurement
- ☐ Fractions, Decimals, Ratios, and Percents
- ☐ Probability
- ☐ Patterns and Motion in Geometry

Notes

_____

_____

_____

_____

Goals

_____

_____

_____

_____

Study Planner

Sunday	Monday	Tuesday	Wednesday	Thursday	Friday	Saturday

Study Topic Checklist

- ☐ Patterns in Mathematics
- ☐ Numeration
- ☐ Data Management
- ☐ Addition and Subtraction
- ☐ Measuring Length
- ☐ Multiplication and Division
- ☐ 2-D Geometry
- ☐ Area
- ☐ Multiplying Decimals
- ☐ Dividing Decimals
- ☐ 3-D Geometry and 3-D Measurement
- ☐ Fractions, Decimals, Ratios, and Percents
- ☐ Probability
- ☐ Patterns and Motion in Geometry

Notes

_____

_____

_____

_____

Goals

_____

_____

_____

_____

Multiplication Table

1	1	2	3	4	5	6	7	8	9	10	11	12
1	1	2	3	4	5	6	7	8	9	10	11	12
2	2	4	6	8	10	12	14	16	18	20	22	24
3	3	6	9	12	15	18	21	24	27	30	33	36
4	4	8	12	16	20	24	28	32	36	40	44	48
5	5	10	15	20	25	30	35	40	45	50	55	60
6	6	12	18	24	30	36	42	48	54	60	66	72
7	7	14	21	28	35	42	49	56	63	70	77	84
8	8	16	24	32	40	48	56	64	72	80	88	96
9	9	18	27	36	45	54	63	72	81	90	99	108
10	10	20	30	40	50	60	70	80	90	100	110	120
11	11	22	33	44	55	66	77	88	99	110	121	132
12	12	24	36	48	60	72	84	96	108	120	132	144